REGENERATION

AND INNOVATION

First published in 2011 by Libri Publishing

Copyright © Jim Lewis

ISBN 978 1 907471 56 8

A CIP catalogue record for this book is available from The British Library

Design by Helen Taylor

Maps by Alice Gadney of Silver7 Mapping Ltd

Printed in the UK by Ashford Colour Press

Libri Publishing
Brunel House
Volunteer Way
Faringdon
Oxfordshire
SN7 7YR

Tel: +44 (0)845 873 3837
www.libripublishing.co.uk

REGENERATION
AND INNOVATION

Invention and reinvention
in the Lea Valley

Jim Lewis

LIBRI
PUBLISHING

SPONSOR PROFILE

Libri Publishing was supported in the publication of this book by Lee Valley Estates.

Dear Reader

It is a great privilege to write a few words to preface this book which recalls the truly great heritage of innovation in the Lea Valley. A natural part of innovation is regeneration and this part of London has always been at the forefront of moving forward and providing new industry and opportunities to serve its community.

We, at Lee Valley Estates, are very proud to be part of this and the regeneration of Tottenham Hale is a good example of a community embracing change for the benefit of future generations.

Many people are unaware of the fact that Tottenham Hale plays and always has played a key part in the development of the Lea Valley and North East London. From the time of the Danes it has been a crossing and was a very important early transport node. It is an exceptional place; the heart of regeneration in North East London.

The rebirth of Tottenham Hale is happening due to its unique characteristics which are little known to many people. It:

- adjoins all the reservoirs that serve the entire capital and which provide great leisure opportunities
- affords easy access to all points of central London
- is within easy travelling time of no fewer than three International Airports serving London
- gives direct access to the largest shopping precinct in Europe, Westfield Stratford, some 10 minutes away
- is adjacent to the 10,000-acre Lee Valley Park, which runs from Ware in the north down to the Olympic Village in the south
- adjoins an eight-acre nature reserve, The Paddocks and Walthamstow Wetlands which covers 440 acres
- is served by both main line and Underground rail connections that are unsurpassed
- is in close proximity to the UK Motorway system
- is home to one of the most successful retail parks in North London.

Lee Valley Estates purchased the site (now known as Hale Village) in 2004 from Middlesex University with the vision of creating a new affordable, vibrant community by 2015. This dream is now coming to fruition and will result in a complete community that will work in harmony with its neighbours to create a model of sustainable regeneration. The aspiration is to produce homes, offices and jobs for local people, residences for 1,300 students, a health centre, local shops, a gymnasium, parks, and roof allotments.

It would be wrong for me not to thank sincerely all those colleagues who have done so much to ensure the success of our initiative. The people who have made Hale Village work are too numerous to mention. However, I believe I must extend particular thanks to the following colleagues: Chris Shellard, Gary Walker, Nigel Fletcher, and Matthew Loughlin in the Lee Valley Estates team, all our private sector partners, David Lunts, Nick Taylor, Sir Peter Rogers, Claire Kober, Mark Dorfman, Mike Hinch and Richard Simpson from the public sector and David Lammy, our local MP.

Without all of them the transformation of Tottenham Hale and the creation of Hale Village would not have been possible.

Lee Valley Estates is very pleased to support Jim Lewis's book, which allows the reader to not only understand the past but also see that the future is bright for both living and working in the Lea Valley.

Michael Polledri MBE

Chairman, Lee Valley Estates

June 2011

Creating Enterprising Communities

Hale Village, May 2011

DEDICATION

This book is dedicated to my family and also to my late mother and father, Leonora Maud Lewis and Walter Harry Portman Lewis.

ABOUT THE AUTHOR

Dr Jim Lewis has spent most of his career in the consumer electronics industry, apart from a three-year spell in the Royal Air Force servicing airborne and ground wireless communications equipment. When working in the Lea Valley for Thorn EMI Ferguson he represented the company abroad on several occasions and was involved in the exchange of manufacturing technology. Currently he is a Consultant to Terry Farrell & Partners on the historical development of London's Lea Valley and a Workers' Educational Association (WEA) tutor teaching industrial history. He also teaches students within the Community Programme who have learning difficulties. A freelance writer, researcher and broadcaster for his specialist subject – London's Lea Valley – he also has a genuine passion for encouraging partnership projects within the local community, which in the long term are planned to help stimulate social and economic regeneration. Dr Lewis is married with four grown-up children and lives in Lincolnshire.

The author Dr Jim Lewis on the roof of Alexandra Palace, Wood Green, below the iconic mast that once radiated, on Saturday 2 November 1936, the world's first high-definition public-service television broadcast signals to viewers in the London region. Dr Lewis is being interviewed by the journalist and broadcaster Dr Kurt Barling during the making of an item, filmed on the seventieth anniversary of World War Two, for BBC Television News. The piece was to commemorate the role played by the BBC engineers and government scientists who had modified the Alexander Palace television transmitter allowing it to successfully jam one of the most sophisticated aircraft navigational systems employed by the Luftwaffe and installed in certain German Heinkels that were targeting Britain during the height of the Blitz.

SERIES ACKNOWLEDGEMENTS

The author wishes to thank the following organisations, companies and societies for their encouragement, support and advice and for supplying many of the illustrations within this book:

Alexandra Palace and Park Trust, Wood Green, London
BAE Systems, Farnborough, Hampshire
Bishopsgate Institute, London
Black & Ethnic Minority Business Association, Walthamstow, London
BOC Process Plants, Edmonton, London
Brooklands Museum, Weybridge, Surrey
Bruce Castle Museum, Tottenham, London
Civix, Exton Street, London
Corporation of Trinity House, Tower Hill, London
Cuffley Industrial Heritage Society, Cuffley, Hertfordshire
Edmonton Hundred Historical Society, Enfield, Middlesex
Enfield Archaeological Society, Enfield, Middlesex
Enfield Business Centre, Enfield, Middlesex
Enfield Energy Centre Limited, Enfield, Middlesex
Enfield Enterprise Agency, Enfield, Middlesex
Enfield Local History Unit, Enfield, Middlesex
English Heritage, Blandford Street, London
Epping Forest Museum, Waltham Abbey, Essex
Greater London Record Office, Northampton Road, London
Greenwich Industrial History Society, Greenwich
Gunpowder Mills Study Group, Guildford, Surrey
Guy & Wright Ltd., Green Tye, Hertfordshire
Hackney Society, Hackney, London
Harper Collins Publishers, Hammersmith, London
Hawker Siddeley Power Transformers, Walthamstow, London
Historical Publications Ltd., Barnsbury, London
Hornsey Historical Society, Hornsey, London
House of Lords Record Office, Westminster, London
Imperial War Museum, Duxford, Cambridgeshire
Institution of Civil Engineers, George Street, London
Institution of Engineering and Technology, Savoy Place, London
Institution of Mechanical Engineers, Birdcage Walk, London
Jewish Museum, Finchley, London
John Higgs, Freelance Historian, Fairford, Gloucestershire
Johnson Matthey, Enfield, Middlesex
Lea Valley Growers Association, Cheshunt, Hertfordshire
Lee Valley Business and Innovation Centre, Enfield, Middlesex
Lee Valley Estates, Tottenham Hale, London
Lee Valley Regional Park Authority, Enfield, Middlesex
London Borough of Enfield, Enfield, Middlesex
London Borough of Haringey, Haringey, London
London Borough of Newham, East Ham, London
London Borough of Waltham Forest, Walthamstow, London
London Lee Valley Partnership Limited, Great Eastern Street, London
London Organising Committee of the Olympic & Paralympic Games, Canary Wharf, London
London Waste Ltd, Edmonton, London

Lotus Engineering, Hethel, Norwich, Norfolk
Marconi Archive, Oxford University Library Services, Oxford, Oxfordshire
Markfield Beam Engine & Museum, Tottenham, London
Midland Publishing Limited, Earl Shilton, Leicester
Ministry of Defence Library, Royal Armouries, Leeds, Yorkshire
Museum of London, London Wall, London
National Archive, Kew, Richmond, Surrey
National Army Museum, Chelsea, London
National Maritime Museum, Greenwich, London
National Portrait Gallery, London
Natural History Museum, Kensington, London
Navtech Systems Ltd., Market Harborough, Leicestershire
New River Action Group, Hornsey, London
Newham Local History Library, Stratford, London
North London Strategic Alliance, Wood Green, London
Perkins Group, Leyton, London
Phillips Auctioneers & Valuers, New Bond Street, London
Potters Bar Historical Society, Potters Bar, Hertfordshire
Pump House Steam & Transport Museum, Walthamstow, London
RCHME Cambridge, (National Monuments Record), Cambridge, Cambridgeshire
Reuters Limited, Fleet Street, London
River Lea Tidal Mill Trust, Bromley-by-Bow, London
Royal Air Force Museum, Hendon, London
Royal Commission on Historic Manuscripts, Quality Court, Chancery Lane, London
Royal Society of Chemistry, Burlington House, London
Royal Television Society, Holborn Hall, London
Science Museum, Kensington, London
Scout Association, Chingford, Essex
Southgate District Civic Trust, Southgate, London
Siemens United Kingdom, Frimley, Camberley, Surrey
Speedway Museum, Broxbourne, Hertfordshire
Stratford City Challenge, Stratford, London
Tesco, Cheshunt, Hertfordshire
Thames Water, Reading, Berkshire
Thorn EMI Archive, Hayes, Middlesex
Tower Hamlets Local History Library, Tower Hamlets, London
University of Leicester Space Research Group, Leicester, Leicestershire
Upper Lee Valley Partnership, Tottenham Hale, London
Valley Grown Nurseries, Nazeing, Essex
Vauxhall Heritage, Luton, Bedfordshire
Eric Verdon-Roe, grandson of Alliott Verdon-Roe
Vestry House Museum, Walthamstow, London
Waltham Abbey Royal Gunpowder Mills Company Ltd., Waltham Abbey, Essex
Walthamstow Amateur Cine Video Club, Walthamstow, London
WEA, London District, Luke Street, London
Wordsworth Editions, Ware, Hertfordshire

While many individuals have freely given their knowledge, some unknowingly, which
has contributed greatly to the production of this series of books, I have, on a number
of occasions paid special tribute to certain people in the footnotes of various
chapters.

I could not let the occasion pass without recording my sincere thanks to my wife
Jenny for her superb editorial skills and outstanding patience. The author freely
admits that this voluntary sacrifice on Jenny's part has comprehensively tested the
cement that holds our wonderful marriage together.

AUTHOR'S NOTE

Events such as the Olympics can be brought into our homes and workplaces from the host country as they take place through the power of electronic communication – radio, television, the Internet and satellite broadcasts. The technology that allowed this to happen was first discovered and developed at Ponders End, Enfield in London's Lea Valley.

In November 1904, after much experiment, Professor Ambrose Fleming registered his patent for the diode valve, the world's first thermionic device. This inspired invention not only paved the way for today's multimedia electronics industry, but also created the delivery platform for space travel, e-mail and the Internet, not to mention computers.

Thirty-two years after Fleming's invention, in November 1936, the world's first high-definition public service television broadcasts were transmitted by the BBC from Alexandra Palace, positioned on the crest of the Lea Valley's western slopes.

Centring the 2012 Olympic and Paralympic Games in London's Lea Valley will provide a unique opportunity to remind the world that it was the development of electronic communication within the region that has allowed the participating nations to share the message of peace and friendship.

Jim Lewis

CONTENTS

INTRODUCTION

It is probably fair to say that authors who research interesting and little-known historical subjects tend to resist the requests of their readers to produce yet another book highlighting new facts. Then, as in my case, the pressure becomes too great and the research bullet has to be bitten. Once the decision is made there is no turning back and the author is faced with months, sometimes years, of archive research to follow up reader leads and to see if sufficient material exists in a particular subject area to construct an interesting and worthwhile story. While the prospect of the challenge at first may appear daunting, once fully committed and immersed in the work the excitement level builds and it is particularly satisfying when new information comes to light.

In my last three books, I invited readers, particularly teachers and school children, to get involved in Lea Valley projects and also to take on the role of detectives to discover if more interesting stories existed about the region. Some schools and universities rose to the challenge and on a number of occasions I was invited to become involved and also to act as a Lea Valley tour guide. It is occasions like these that make writing doubly rewarding.

Due to considerable local interest, and also the requests by many retailers for reprints of earlier material, the author has been persuaded to deviate from the intentions of the original format used in my earlier Lea Valley books, that of keeping chapters deliberately short, and for this new series I shall include a fuller treatment of many of the subjects. Therefore, it is intended to give each book in the series a particular theme. In this way it is hoped that that the readers' requests will be largely satisfied and also a greater insight into the developments of the region will be achieved.

I have been greatly encouraged to be quoted by prominent writers and broadcasters such as Ian Sinclair and also to receive letters from Dr Adam Hart-Davis saying "I had no idea that the great George Parker Bidder was, no less, 'the maker of modern West Ham'. I told the story in the wilds of Moretonhampstead." The BBC newscaster Mike Embly, once referred to me as the "Lea Valley alarm clock" as

I appear to wake people up to the historic significance of the region. These compliments make the long hours in front of a computer screen and the many years of archive research seem worthwhile and this encourages me to discover and write more about the Lea Valley, its entrepreneurs and its world firsts. Perhaps, sometime in the future the region will no longer be Britain's best-kept secret.

As I am mindful that the forthcoming Olympics will bring many people to the Lea Valley from around the world, who will want to learn a little more about the region, I have decided to include some stories to attract those readers with broader interests beyond that of the subject of industrial heritage.

Jim Lewis

1. THE DEMISE AND RISE OF TOTTENHAM HALE – A STORY OF SEVERAL PARTS

POSSIBLE ORIGINS OF THE NAME

The district, or hamlet, of Tottenham Hale is thought to have acquired its name from the Old English word 'hale', meaning to hoist or drag. Labourers would have had to hoist, or perhaps use a hoist to lift, timber from the barges that were moored on the River Lea that runs north–south through the area. Barges that were docked at Tottenham Hale were able to have their cargoes of timber and other goods transferred to wagons for onward transportation by road. Therefore, it is easy to see how the connection could have been made between the physical effort of handling the heavy planks of wood and other goods and the naming of the place. However, there is also another school of thought which suggests that the name comes from the ferry that once had to be 'hailed' before a bridge was built over the River Lea at what is now Ferry Lane, one of the few transport routes across the Lea Valley.

A tile picture on the wall of Tottenham Hale Victoria Line Underground Station depicting the scene of a ferry crossing the River Lea that would have had to be 'hailed'.

MILLING AT TOTTENHAM HALE

Looking for evidence of early industry at Tottenham Hale, there is no mention of a mill in the Domesday Book; there is merely a reference to the Countess Judith holding various parcels of land and also a number of different domestic animals for the King. The first reference to a water mill in the area appears in 1234, almost 150 years after the Domesday survey took place. Another early reference to a mill, entered in the Tottenham Manor Court Rolls, occurs in 1367 when Thomas Hardynge is recorded as carrying clay and earth and also digging turfs to repair the wall of a water mill as part of his service to the Lord.

There is also a rather humorous story, which occurs around the beginning of the seventeenth century, concerning a leather mill that once stood on the River Lea at Tottenham. In those days it was normal for tradesmen, in the process of leather-making, to use oil in the treatment of the animal skins to ensure they became supple. On this particular occasion it would appear their choice of oil was somewhat questionable. At a time when King James I was travelling north along the main road, now Tottenham High Road, presumably on his way to his country retreat at Theobalds Palace, Cheshunt (this was the estate which he had recently exchanged for Hatfield House, Hertfordshire, with his Secretary of State, Sir Robert Cecil), the Privy Council gave the order for the mill to stop working. This was done on the grounds that the King would be passing some eight hundred metres to the west and the smell that emanated from the mill's leather-processing operation was apparently too pungent for his sensitive nose. This would suggest that on the day of the King's planned passing the prevailing wind was from the east and wafting the noxious odour across the Lea Valley. Hopefully today's royalty are made of much stronger stuff!

In 1656, there are further references to the mills at Tottenham producing gunpowder instead of flour and by the 1730s it is suggested that the mills were then involved in the manufacture of paper. While such changes of use might seem odd to the casual observer, it is not unusual to see different products being processed over the lifetime of a mill as the miller would seek to supplement, or enhance, his income by the most economic means possible. Researchers, by studying these milling changes, can often gain vital clues to what was happening in the wider historical landscape at the time. For example, if a flour mill starts processing gunpowder it is often a sign that the country has become involved in a war and under such circumstances every means possible has to be found to manufacture the explosive for the army and the navy. It was a similar story for manufacturers who had factories in the area at the time of the First and Second World Wars (see later in this chapter). It is probably no coincidence that, about the time when the Tottenham mill went over to gunpowder production, Britain was heavily involved in the First Anglo-Dutch War (1652–4), the Anglo-Spanish War (1656–9) and the Second Anglo-Dutch War (1665–7). The need to supply the armed forces with gunpowder from every possible production source would have been crucial, as at the time there were no single suppliers of explosives in Britain that could have coped with the increase in demand.

Research by staff at Bruce Castle Museum has discovered that the Tottenham mills were burned down in 1778 then later rebuilt. In 1816 the mills were badly damaged when the region was affected by serious flooding. In 1860, a disastrous fire again took its toll and the mills were destroyed, never to be rebuilt. However, the Museum has confirmed that the remains of the mills could still be seen on the River Lea at Tottenham Hale up until the 1920s.

INDUSTRIAL CHANGE

For many decades local people and regular visitors to Tottenham Hale have witnessed a continuing downturn in the region's one-

An early-nineteenth-century etching of the Tottenham Mills on the River Lea at Tottenham Hale.

time vibrant manufacturing and wealth-creating industries. Household names like Lebus (furniture), Gestetner (duplicators and copiers), Keith Blackman (industrial fans), Berol (pencils), ELAC (loudspeakers), Cannon (rubber products), A.W. Flatau (boot and shoemakers) and GLS (distribution depot for goods and equipment to schools within the former Greater London Council region) have all vanished from the landscape. These industries and the depot created employment and generated wealth not just for Tottenham residents but also those living within the Lea Valley region and beyond.

Tottenham Mills painted by John Bonny in the late nineteenth century.

Tottenham Lock, Tottenham Hale about 1920.

Currently (2010) a major regeneration scheme is taking place on land once owned by Harris Lebus, formerly one of the world's largest furniture manufacturers and it is the wish of the developer, Lee Valley Estates, that the history of this company is recorded for the community.

HARRIS LEBUS – MAKER OF AFFORDABLE FURNITURE

In the 1840s, Louis Lebus, who appears to have been one of the earliest Jewish immigrant furniture workers to have come to Britain, arrived in Hull from Breslau in Germany. By 1857 he had set up a workshop to pursue his craft in Whitechapel, in London's East End. His business must have been relatively successful as in 1875 he moved to larger premises in Stepney, now in the London Borough of Tower Hamlets.

After Louis's death in 1879 the business was taken over by his twenty-seven-year-old son Harris who in 1885 moved the firm yet again to a multi-storey building in Tabernacle Street. This was closer to Curtain Road in the district of Shoreditch where many of the East End's furniture and associated industries were concentrated.

An interesting fact was brought to the attention of the author by William Massil, a former manufacturer of turned wooden parts for the industry. He explained that in the early nineteenth century the mainly small craft workshops which made up the furniture trade were divided between two distinct areas of London. There were those businesses in the West End, which were referred to as the "honourable" side, while those in the East End were known as the "dishonourable" side. Massil suggests that it was the West End manufacturers who supplied the prestigious London retailers until the middle of the nineteenth century, but then it became the turn of the East End furniture trade to take over as the main suppliers. According to Massil, the perceived notion that the West End produced the best quality furniture while the East End manufactured the cheap is totally erroneous. There were, he remarked, considerable variations in quality within both sectors of the industry.

Off-loading timber from a barge on the Lee Navigation into the Lebus Ferry Lane storage and drying sheds, Tottenham Hale, c.1950.

A Lebus dining-room suite in the classic mid-1950s style. These suites were extremely popular with post-war families.

A view from the air of the Harris Lebus factory, c.1950. In the foreground and to the left can be seen the vast area of drying sheds that once stood next to Ferry Lane. Housing estates now cover the former Lebus site to the east and west of the Lee Navigation.

Harris Lebus (1852–1907) from his obituary in the journal *The Cabinet Maker*, 28 September 1907.

Looking north across the Lebus factory roof-tops showing the company name prominently displayed on a chimney.

A Lebus advertisement from the trade journal *The Cabinet Maker*, 19 July 1947, claiming the Finsbury Works at Tottenham to be "The Largest Furniture Factory in the World".

An advertisement for Gibbons of Hackney, established 1831, from a Lebus trade brochure that was produced to promote one of its valued furniture dealers. The Gibbons family sold the store to a private property company in 2002 and in June 2003 the building was destroyed by fire.

A piece of Lebus furniture in the arts and crafts style which has now become a popular item with collectors.

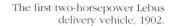

The first two-horsepower Lebus delivery vehicle, 1902.

The progress of the Harris Lebus business was slightly delayed in 1894 by a serious fire. After rebuilding, the firm became the largest furniture manufacturer in Britain, employing in excess of one thousand workers by the end of the century. By 1900, further manufacturing expansion to meet the long-term consumer demand for furniture was out of the question in the cramped streets of the East End. Therefore, the decision was taken to build a new factory on a thirteen-and-a-half acre green-field site by the River Lea at Tottenham. Subsequently more land was purchased which increased the area of the site to forty acres. The East End premises in Tabernacle Street were not abandoned but converted to showrooms to display Lebus products.

Many other East End furniture firms, looking to expand, followed the example of Lebus and established themselves on other sites in the upper Lea Valley where land was relatively cheap. There they discovered how useful the river was, as timber could be brought by barge directly from the London Docks and stored in warehouses beside the waterway where it could dry until required for manufacture. The new Lebus factory was completed by 1904. However, the majority of the workforce had to commute by public transport from the East End. This arrangement proved unsatisfactory for many, so Lebus encouraged the building of houses nearby which promoted the growth of south Tottenham.

WORLD WAR ONE

During the First World War (1914–18), like many other manufacturers, Lebus became involved in war work. Also like other manufacturers, Lebus was not alone in losing male workers to the armed forces. This loss of labour created formidable problems for industry and in such volatile times solutions have to be found. In the case of the departing manpower, it was women-power that came to the rescue. With training, women soon became proficient in just about every skill that their male counterparts possessed. However, what the author finds remarkable is that it has taken almost one hundred years, well into the twenty-first century, for women to begin to gain the recognition they deserved for acquiring these hard-won skills. However, in many cases, they have still to reach parity of pay when performing the same workplace tasks as their male counterparts.

Women workers at Lebus constructed tents for the military, made ammunition boxes capable of holding six-hundred rounds apiece, constructed and prepared large sections of such aircraft as the Handley Page 0/100 and the V/1500 bi-plane, they also covered and doped (a process of painting or spraying the covering fabric with a type of varnish) wings of the Vickers Vimy, a heavy twin-engine bomber.

Women tent-bottom makers at the Lebus factory during World War One.

A First World War Handley Page bomber. Large sections of this aircraft were built at the Lebus factory.

Wings of a Vickers Vimy aircraft being covered with fabric at the Lebus factory during the First World War.

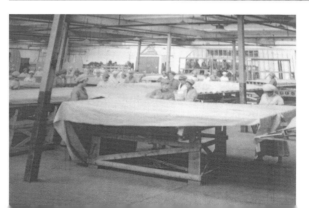

Operators doping the wings of a model 0400 Handley Page bomber at the Lebus factory during the First World War.

Ammunition boxes manufactured at the Lebus factory during the First World War.

Interestingly, it was a modified Vickers Vimy that was the first aircraft to cross the Atlantic non-stop in June 1919, piloted by Captain John Alcock and navigated by Lieutenant Arthur Whitton-Brown. The aircraft took off from St John's, Newfoundland and crash landed in a bog at Clifden, County Galway, Ireland. The flight of 1,890 miles took just under sixteen hours and at take-off the aircraft was carrying 865 gallons of aviation fuel. For its day, this was a truly remarkable achievement as the Wright brothers had only succeeded in the first recorded powered flight less than sixteen years before. During the subsequent years the speed of technological change really gathered pace: only seventy years after the Alcock and Brown Atlantic crossing, the American astronaut Neil Armstrong walked on the surface of the moon.

An Airspeed Horsa glider. Many of these aircraft were built at the Lebus factory during the Second World War.

A Second World War De Havilland Mosquito (the wooden wonder) under construction at the Lebus factory.

In the future it would be nice to think that a student researching early aviation history might stumble across information suggesting that the Vickers Vimy, flown by Alcock and Brown, owed its origins to the women workers of Lebus!

WORLD WAR TWO

As well as the owners, many of the workers in Britain's furniture industry were Jewish immigrants who had left Europe to avoid persecution. They had arrived in Britain with little more than the skills they possessed. It was perhaps somewhat ironic that these skills, and those passed down from the earlier immigrants, would become a vital asset in the struggle against Nazism when several of the Lea Valley furniture factories were taken over by the British government to supplement the needs of the Allied Forces by becoming engaged in war work.

By the start of the Second World War the Lebus factory employed almost 8,000 people, later confidentially claiming in its advertising literature to be the largest furniture manufacturer in the world. During the hostilities of 1939–45 the factory, then run by Herman Lebus (later Sir), played a major part in the war effort by manufacturing sections of aeroplanes such as the de Havilland Mosquito, the Horsa Glider and replica Sherman tanks from wood. These were used as decoys to fool the enemy, particularly Luftwaffe pilots flying over Britain, into thinking that Britain's military might was much greater than it really was. Other essential equipment and

munitions were also manufactured at the Tottenham Hale factory for the Allied Forces.

Harris Lebus would no doubt have been justly proud to have seen the expansion of the furniture industry out of the East End to sites in the upper Lea Valley where it grew and flourished. Sadly his premature death in 1907 at the age of fifty-five did not allow this.

INDUSTRY IN DECLINE

By 1969, and after the death of Sir Herman Lebus, the long-established family-run firm had left Tottenham, signalling the decline of the Lea Valley furniture industry. The Lebus southern and northern sites were eventually acquired by the Greater London Council which was responsible for the demolition of the factory and also the timber storage and drying sheds which lined the eastern bank of the Lee Navigation. On the cleared land on the southern site the erection of a large housing development took place which became known as the Ferry Lane housing estate. The large Lebus distribution depot on the northern site was not demolished.

By the start of the 1980s the demise of the Lea Valley furniture industry had escalated and it was clear that recovery was impossible. The decline had been brought about by a combination of events. These ranged from the increasing pressure on the home industry from cheap imports, to the changing pattern of retail sales which began to move away from the traditional high street furniture shop to the new superstores that were becoming increasingly popular with post-war upwardly mobile car owners. Ironically, several of these new furniture superstores have begun to occupy the space, left on industrial estates, where furniture factories once stood and thrived.

There are still a few remnants of the wood and furniture industry surviving in the Lea Valley today, although representing only a shadow of the former glory days of large-scale manufacturing. Also there are a modest number of craft-based workshops scattered throughout the region, carrying on the trade with the skills handed down from the early immigrants, a powerful reminder to us all of the magnificent contribution made to Britain by this resilient group of people. Perhaps what is also remarkable is that there appears to be a growing interest in old Lebus furniture as collectors' items. A number of auction houses around the world are now offering various pieces of the furniture for sale and this would have no doubt brought a wry smile to the face of the late Harris Lebus who had striven to bring good quality affordable furniture to the masses.

GREATER LONDON COUNCIL STORES (GLS)

After the demolition of the Lebus buildings on the south side of Ferry Lane, the large architect-designed building on the north side, built in 1958 only eleven years before Lebus vacated Tottenham, was retained and used as a distribution depot by the Greater London Council (GLC) for supplying goods and equipment to schools within the Inner London Education Authority (ILEA) area.

Trying to trace local people with knowledge or those who had worked at the depot has not been easy. Even pursuing enquiries with the help of Bruce Castle Museum and through other local sources has not proved particularly fruitful. However, the author was fortunate in tracing Barry Robinson who had worked in the butchery department of the GLS from 1984 until 1987. Barry confirmed that at the time of his employment ten people worked in the department preparing, weighing and packing meat and bacon under the watchful eye of the department's head, Bob Daton. These along with different meat products and a range of other foodstuffs, were dispatched daily to kitchens within the region to be prepared by cooks and ancillary staff into traditional school meals that were either loved or hated by the children that received them.

The GLS building at Tottenham Hale under demolition.

The GLS depot was responsible for stocking and delivering a vast selection of other goods and equipment to schools. These ranged from stationery, pencils and pens to furniture and classroom equipment. The depot was very much a self-contained operation running and

Loading a pallet onto a lorry ready for despatch at the GLS depot, Tottenham Hale.

The material storage and handling department at the GLS depot, Tottenham Hale.

Quantities of the foodstuff held at the GLS depot Tottenham Hale for distribution to schools in the Greater London area.

A Vauxhall Bedford truck that was part of the GLS delivery fleet.

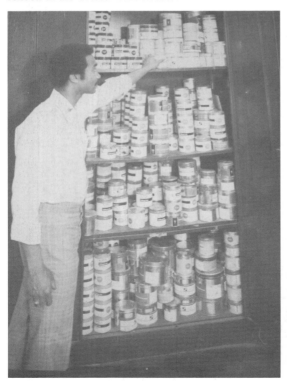

The GLS depot butchery department at Tottenham Hale.

The former GLS building at Tottenham Hale when it was being let out as low-cost business units.

The GLS depot print shop at Tottenham Hale.

maintaining its own transport fleet and, because of its relative size, it was able to act as a central purchasing body, buying goods in bulk and thereby providing a cost-effective service to the schools within its catchment area.

In 1986 the Greater London Council was abolished, although the ILEA carried on for a little longer until it was disbanded in 1990. In its place the individual London boroughs took responsibility for education in their own areas and the GLS depot became surplus to requirements as it could no longer perform its former role. Over the years the building went through many changes of use from laying empty for some time, to providing relatively cheap accommodation for a number of small firms who were able to carry on their individual businesses, to acting as a store place for various materials. Although local groups and politicians suggested a number of possible uses for the building, none came to fruition. Fortunately, in 2006, after much discussion, consultation and research, Lee Valley Estates came to the rescue with an innovative, imaginative and ambitious plan.

DISCOVERING A FORGOTTEN LANDSCAPE

Before demolition of the former GLS warehouse, Lee Valley Estates commissioned a leading firm of consultants, CgMs, to carry out a detailed archaeological survey of the former Lebus north site with a view to establishing what lay beneath the ground. Although Lee Valley Estates had a genuine interest in discovering the archaeology on what was planned to become a major construction site, it should be remembered that it is now a requirement for developers to have an archaeological survey carried out before commencement of any large-scale building projects. In this way we can all feel confident that our precious lost heritage is being discovered, interpreted and recorded.

In January 2007 an archaeological survey began on the former Harris Lebus north site where the factory warehouse and distribution depot stood and which was subsequently used by GLS. The first work carried out by the archaeologists was an initial assessment and this was done via a series of three targeted holes cut by machine through the concrete over-site before the standing structures were cleared. This work exposed arched concrete structures located approximately 1.8 metres below the surface level and these were broken open to allow ladder access. A preliminary survey in the year 2000 had been carried out by Arup Associates and a subsequent documentary investigation showed that an extensive network of linear features existed below ground. While this information was clearly helpful to the archaeologists,

Below: The massive Lebus underground air raid shelter complex being exposed after breaking through the concrete in 2007.

Below right: Underground toilets discovered by archaeologists when they excavated the Lebus factory air raid shelter in 2007.

they reported that "it lacked any detail or notation to suggest that they were buried structures". Once the entrances had been exposed it became clear that an extensive network of tunnels existed. However, before the archaeologists could proceed further the specialist firm of Fellows International PLC were called in to carry out an unexploded ordnance and air quality survey. Once Fellows had given the all clear the archaeological team began work, but not before the necessary health and safety precautions had been taken to protect the archaeologists while they were below ground.

A partly drained tunnel in the Lebus factory underground air raid shelter complex.

Exit directions painted on the wall of the Lebus underground air raid shelter.

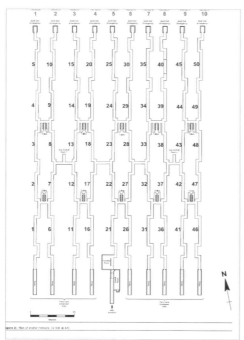

A plan of the vast complex of underground air raid shelters that were built to protect the Lebus workforce during the Second World War.

A collection of rusting Home Guard (Dad's Army) helmets that were discovered amongst the various artefacts in the Lebus underground air raid shelters.

Fragments of china from the Lebus canteen, discovered during the excavation of the underground air raid shelter in 2007.

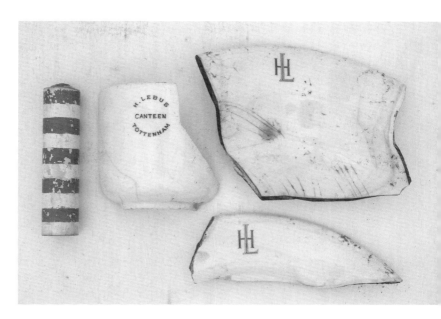

Deborah Hedgecock, curator of Bruce Castle Museum, with archaeologists during the excavation of the GLS site in 2007.

On entering the tunnel network, which was flooded to depths of up to 1.2 metres, the archaeologists discovered what would eventually turn out to be a massive air-raid shelter complex, built to protect the workforce of the Harris Lebus factory during the bombing raids of the Second World War. Once the water was pumped out, a system of ten 'trench shelters' was revealed. Each trench contained five separate shelters measuring 20 metres in length by 1.5 metres in width. Within the complex there were toilets, sleeping areas, a first-aid room, control and sub-control rooms that were linked to the factory and to other outside areas by telephone. Evidence was also discovered of the remains of a surface look-out post that had been removed, presumably sometime after the war. Among the many artefacts that were found was a John Player's Navy Cut cigarette packet, a selection of glass bottles and a collection of rusting Home Guard helmets.

At a meeting at Bruce Castle Museum on 25 September 2008 attended by members of the Lebus family, the late Oliver Lebus, grandson of Harris, explained that "Because of the scale of the factory it would have taken people many minutes to reach the air-raid shelters, so other shelters were built above ground for each workshop. After that local people were always welcome to take shelter in the underground tunnels".

What the author finds remarkable was that when the construction of these shelters was complete in 1939, the then Minister for Home Security with responsibility for Air Raid Precautions (ARP), Sir John Anderson, came to Tottenham Hale to open the complex officially. The event was reported in the *Tottenham & Edmonton Weekly Herald* (4 August 1939) under the heading "Factory's Row of A.R.P. Trenches" and went on to proclaim that "Civil Defence Minister Sir John Anderson, the Lord Privy Seal, came to Tottenham on Friday at the invitation of Mr. R.C. Morrison, M.P. (chairman of the Borough A.R.P. Organisation), and inspected what he described as the finest system of underground air-raid shelters he had seen in any industrial establishment". Also on the same day a similar report appeared in the *Jewish Chronicle*, under the heading "Jewish Firm Leads In A.R.P. Protection For Furniture Trade Workers". With Britain about to enter the Second World War with Germany, the publicity given to the air-raid shelter does appear extremely foolhardy as it would appear to have made the Lebus factory a potential Luftwaffe target. Given such blatant publicity it would be hard to imagine that German intelligence networks would not have been aware of this story and it would have been logical for them to have reasoned that the building of such a vast complex of shelters for the Lebus workers was an indication that the factory was gearing up for major war work.

John Anderson (1882–1958), Minister of Civil Defence during the Second World War.

THE REBIRTH OF TOTTENHAM HALE

Having a vision is one thing, but transforming the idea into reality usually takes a little longer. In 2006 Lee Valley Estates (LVE) submitted a planning application to Haringey Council for the redevelopment of the Tottenham Hale GLS site and by May 2007 the entire scheme had received outline approval. A design code was produced to ensure all the buildings conformed to the highest design standards. Following the production of the design code a number of detailed consents were obtained with only the design of the residential tower under consideration. Later that year planning consent was given for the construction of 1,200 units of high-quality student accommodation and also for the building of the necessary roads, sewers and drains. In addition to this, approval was granted to install an innovative combined heat and power system (CHP) and also a rainwater harvesting facility that would complement the plan for the site's overall green credentials. The CHP system employs a woodchip burning boiler which uses locally

open space, probably by the expansion of Down Lane Park and to relocate the Ashley Road Council rubbish tip to another site within the borough. This would then free up land for the proposed housing development scheme. The former Berol building, named after the nineteenth-century German pencil maker, Heinrich Berolzheimer, whose family manufactured the famous Eagle pencil and other products there, would remain and become a powerful symbol of Tottenham Hale's proud industrial heritage.

As the regeneration of Tottenham Hale appears to be a central plank in Haringey Council's master plan, the local authority has pledged to keep the community fully informed regarding the proposed developments and also to involve them in the consultation process. Only history will decide if this pledge has been fully honoured, although it is probably fair to conclude that the eventual outcomes will not satisfy everybody. This is to be expected as most planning

The premises situated on the corner of the side road were once the ELAC loudspeaker factory in Broad Lane, Tottenham.

Below: On the right of this picture can be seen two of the remaining poles that once carried the overhead electrical wires that supplied power to the London Transport trolley busses. How many local people have walked past these artefacts and not appreciated what they were?

Below: Tottenham Lock, Tottenham Hale in the 1950s. Note the horses to the left and the trolley bus passing over the Ferry Lane bridge.

consultations end in compromise and, if we are honest, we are all wary of the need for change. However, while it is important to treasure our heritage, we must all learn lessons from the past for in this way we can support our communities to build a better future.

REFERENCES

Author unknown, 'Tottenham's Future Jobs, Who Decides?', Tottenham Employment Group, February 1979

Author unknown, 'Factory's Row of A.R.P. Trenches', *Tottenham & Edmonton Weekly Herald*, 4 August 1939

Author unknown, 'Jewish Firm Leads in A.R.P. Protection for Furniture Workers', *Jewish Chronicle*, 4 August 1939

Author unknown, *Village News*, newsletter of Lee Valley Estates, issue one, April 2007

Author unknown, *Village News*, newsletter of Lee Valley Estates, issue two, March 2008

Author unknown, *Village News*, newsletter of Lee Valley Estates, issue three, June 2008

Conversation with Deborah Hedgecock and Robert Waite, Curator and Deputy Curator, Bruce Castle Museum, June 2010

Conversation with Jon Lowe, Heritage Collective LLP, senior archaeologist responsible for investigating the former Lebus site, July 2010 (also acknowledging Jon Lowe for generously supplying diagrams and photographs from his personal dig archive)

Conversation with senior planners, Haringey Council Planning & Regeneration Department, 639 High Road, Tottenham, London N17 8BD, June 2010

Hillier, Nancy, 'Harris Lebus – Arts and Crafts Style for Trade', *American Bungalow Magazine*, May 2010

Interview with William I. Massil, London, 11 February 1998

Lowe, Jon, Historic Building Record (Site Code: FYN07), in respect of World War II Trench Shelters, Former Harris Lebus Furniture Factory, Ferry Lane, Tottenham, N17, on behalf of Hale Village Property LLP (CgMs Ref: JL/AB/8943, July 2009)

Massil, William I., *Immigrant Furniture Workers in London, 1881-1939*, The Jewish Museum in association with the Geffrye Museum, London, 1997

Pears, Elizabeth, 'New Houses for Old Rubbish Tips', *Haringey Independent*, 9 August 2008

Sharman Nick, 'Turning the Tables – Towards a Strategy for the London Furniture Industry', Greater London Enterprise Board, London, 1985

2. PUSHING FORWARD THE BOUNDARIES OF FLIGHT

George Robert Freeman Edwards was born on 9 July 1908 over his father's toyshop at 12 The Parade, Hale End Road, Highams Park, now part of the London Borough of Waltham Forest. For a person who would eventually achieve great things, young George did not have the easiest start in life and neither did he have the ideal upbringing. His twin sister died at birth and two weeks later his mother also died. George's father Edwin did not enjoy particularly good health and probably reasoned that he could not run his shop and look after the boy. He therefore arranged for the child to stay with the boy's late mother's sister and her husband, Sal and Bill Medlock. The couple lived in a terraced house in Handsworth Avenue, a turning off Hale End Road that was conveniently situated almost opposite the toyshop. George's upbringing by his aunt and uncle is remembered with pride and affection as in later life he told Robert Gardner, his biographer, "They were proper working class and had been brought up in the country. He came from Huntingdonshire and was a copper while I was growing up. But their main job was to keep me fed and going".

The former toyshop in Hale End Road, Highams Park over which Sir George Freeman Edwards (1908–2003) was born.

A Waltham Forest Heritage plaque depicting the birthplace of Sir George Edwards on the side of what was formally12 The Parade, now a solicitor's office and renumbered 499 Hale End Road, Highams Park.

Young George's first taste of education was at a local private school run by two elderly ladies whom he recalls as being "really brilliant". Outside the school they ran was a board on which was written, 'The Warner College for Ladies – Little Boys Accepted'. By the age of eleven, with money becoming tight, George was sent to the nearby elementary school in Selwyn Avenue, a school that still stands today. As George was a bright pupil with a very good mathematical mind, an application was made to the Sir George Monoux grammar school in Chingford Road, Walthamstow for him to sit the entrance exam. Unfortunately George's birthday fell a few days too late for him to qualify for acceptance and the application was duly rejected.

As often happens in life, sometimes a disappointment turns out to be a lucky twist of fate and the episode gave George the opportunity to win a scholarship to the Walthamstow Technical Institute of Engineering and Trade School. The school, as shown on an 1840 map, was situated on the south side of Hoe Street in Grosvenor House (approximately opposite the present Grosvenor Park Road) and was eventually absorbed into what became the South West Essex Technical College in Forest Road, affectionately known as the 'Tech', when it opened in 1938. Later the Tech became the more familiar Waltham Forest College. In the post-war period the Tech equipped thousands of young people with the necessary National and City & Guilds qualifications that launched many of them on successful career paths in commerce and industry, providing the talent to help run several Lea Valley firms. Many industrialists have mourned the loss of the technical colleges as being the start of the erosion of manufacturing, design and trade skills across Britain today.

While at the Technical Institute, George had his second lucky break when he came into contact with two brilliant mathematics teachers who soon recognised that the lad was quick thinking and possessed a fertile mathematical mind. They encouraged George to delve into higher levels of mathematics and, to provide further stimulation for his talents, he was often asked by his tutors "what would you like to do today?" It seems that he had really gained their respect as an exceptional student and was often given one-to-one tuition. With the school providing further lessons in basic design, chemistry and physics, George's future was now pointing strongly towards a career in engineering.

In 1926, at the age of eighteen, George left the technical school and decided to sit an examination for the post of probationary inspector of engineering at the General Post Office (GPO). Although he passed the examination and was offered a job he instead took a clerical position with the Ocean Accident & Guarantee Corporation in the City of London. Within three months of starting, George's talents were recognised by his employer and he was transferred to another department where he was given the responsibility for the periodic inspection of all machinery under insurance.

After only a year with the firm, George applied for, and got, the position of junior technical engineer at Hay's Wharf in the London docks, a job that he described as "a pretty clear spread of rough engineering". Here he covered a wide range of jobs with responsibilities for testing and certificating cranes, bridges and lifts. This meant he had to check different types of lifting gear and calculate that it was properly stressed. For a young man of twenty this was a considerable responsibility but George seems to have relished the challenge, even that of climbing some of dockland's crane jibs 150 feet above the water, sometimes in the dark.

When the Docks Authority decided to build their own cranes, George volunteered for the job and was able to learn much from working alongside skilled craftsmen. In his own words he explained, "after a time I became a pretty hard-arsed engineer". George clearly relished the work and in 1930 he took the entrance exam for the Institution of Structural Engineers, becoming an Associate Member. While working and taking professional exams George was also studying part-time at the West Ham Municipal College for an external London University degree. In July 1935, George was rewarded for all his hard work and dedication when he was awarded a BSC (Eng), quite an achievement for a working-class lad at the time.

The year 1935 was to be a turning point in George Edwards' life. Early that year, now living in Selwyn Avenue, Highams Park, George had applied for the post of aircraft stressman at Vickers (Aviation) Limited, Weybridge, Surrey. Although he was offered the job by the head of department he turned it down as it only paid £5 a week, the same amount he was getting at the London Docks. However, Vickers must have been impressed with the young man as they later wrote suggesting that he might like to apply for a job as a draughtsman. This he did and at the interview with the head of the drawing office George was offered a further five shillings (25 pence) a week, which he accepted. George was destined to stay with Vickers for the rest of his working life, and would continue his career with the company after it was transformed into the British Aircraft Corporation. In October 1935, at All Saints Church, Highams Park, George Edwards made his next life-changing decision when he married Marjorie Annie 'Dinah' Thurgood, his childhood sweetheart from his days at Selwyn Avenue School. The couple were to be devoted life-long partners.

The first few months spent as a junior draughtsman in the Vickers' drawing office were exceedingly boring for someone of George's intellect, particularly as he had come from a job at the docks where he had been given considerable responsibility. According to George his main work was "drawing little gusset plates like biscuits. For a time I got pretty brassed off with it". Fortunately George stuck with the boring jobs and his perseverance was eventually rewarded when he was promoted to lead a small design section. At the outbreak of the Second World War, Britain was losing considerable shipping tonnage as Germany carried out an intensive mining programme of her sea routes. On instructions from Winston Churchill, then First Sea Lord (Churchill became Prime Minister in May 1940), a meeting was hurriedly convened at Vickers between government officials and others from the Royal Aircraft Establishment at Farnborough to see if a solution could be found. It was eventually agreed that Vickers should have the job of designing a system to detonate mines electro-magnetically (the DWI system, detonation without impact) by having a Wellington bomber fitted with a large electric coil situated beneath the aircraft. The project was officially given to the brilliant engineer Barnes Wallace, designer of the R101 airship and the Wellington bomber, but as Wallace was already engaged in other important work the job came down to George Edwards and his team.

A Wellington bomber fitted with a massive electro-magnetic coil as part of the DWI system (detonation without impact) for exploding enemy mines. George Edwards led a small team of engineers who, in 1939, completed the design of the DWI system in under a month.

This was a high-priority job, started in November 1939, with Churchill personally overseeing the project and according to George Edwards "every day I had to send to Winston Churchill a set of photographs of what had been done, and how much progress I had made since the day before". The work was so urgent that the usual paperwork from the drawing office to the factory, to order the construction and manufacture of prototypes and end products, was dispensed with and George was given total authority to see that all procedures relating to the project were carried out.

The programme of work was to manufacture a forty-eight-foot-diameter aluminium tube to encase an electro-magnetic coil, which would have to be aerodynamically stable and safely and securely attached below the fuselage of a Wellington bomber. A 90kw electric generator, to power the coil, would have to be installed inside the aircraft's fuselage and, of course, the on-board flight instruments would have to be screened, as best as possible, from the magnetic field that the coil created. Edwards and his team worked tirelessly on the project, solving problem after problem as each challenge arose. On 21 December 1939, less than a month after the project began, the first Wellington was fitted with the electro-magnetic mine-detonating system. After flight trials on Salisbury Plain, the device was used successfully to detonate a German mine in the Thames Estuary on 8 January 1940. This was achieved by a Wellington bomber flying at 180 miles per hour in poor weather conditions, only sixty feet above the waves. In all, fifteen Wellingtons were then equipped with the device.

Within months of completing the project, George Edwards was promoted to the important position of Experimental Manager, a position he took up in the spring of 1940. In September that year an air raid, by around twenty German aircraft, killed eighty three workers at the Brooklands' factory and injured a further four hundred. For safety, and also to ensure that further raids would not interrupt the top-secret work of the Experimental Department, Edwards was told to find alternative premises for himself and his team that was away from the main site. This he did and the department was relocated to three hangers with outbuildings that Edwards had got erected on the Foxwarren Estate, almost a mile from the factory.

Early in the war Winston Churchill, by then Prime Minister, appointed Lord Beaverbrook, the proprietor of *Express* newspapers, to the position of Minister of Aircraft Production and this brought George Edwards and the Minister into direct contact. Beaverbrook had the idea that targets in Germany could be destroyed by aircraft flying at around 40,000 feet which he reasoned would keep them out of range of enemy gunfire and above the ceiling of the deadly Luftwaffe fighters. He also thought that the damage inflicted by bombing strategic and sensitive targets would boost British morale. Edwards and his team were given the task of designing an aircraft capable of high-altitude flying, provoking him to comment, "it was my first big job and meant we had got to have a pressurised cabin, which nobody else knew anything about".

The undertaking was a mammoth challenge for any engineering team and the request perhaps demonstrates that government ministers were somewhat out of touch with the realities concerning experimental science and production timescales. Nevertheless, Edwards and his team persevered and came up with the idea to construct a separate cabin capsule that could be pressurised, creating the environment that would allow a crew to breath and work normally, without the restrictions of wearing oxygen masks. A Wellington, with extended wings and improved engines, was made available for the experiments and the team had to devise a means of attaching the capsule in such a way to allow for expansion and contraction of the materials used in both the airframe and the new add-on. As might be imagined, little was known at the time of how materials performed at high altitude in the rarefied atmosphere.

After much experiment, with problems of capsules exploding and leaking, sometimes caused by inadvertently pumping in too much air pressure, most of the teething problems were overcome and a programme of flight trials began. As the engineer responsible for the capsule's overall design, Edwards went on a test flight with a Vickers test pilot, Bob Handasyde. The aircraft flew up and down the Welsh coast at a height of 30,000 feet and Edwards and Handasyde entered the capsule that was pressurised to the equivalent of 8,000 feet. Although there were difficulties experienced by both men entering and leaving the capsule's escape hatch, Edwards was impressed that he could work comfortably inside the enclosure in his shirtsleeves. The project and Beaverbrook's idea of bombing Germany from a height were eventually abandoned, but Edwards and his team had learned much about high-altitude flying and pressurised cabins, and the experience gained and the techniques used would become useful in the design of later aircraft.

There are many stories concerning George Edwards' wartime work, from completing projects with the famous Martin Baker Company

Sir Frank Whittle (1907–1996), inventor of the jet engine, with cigarette in hand, sits next to Sir George Edwards on a Vickers Viscount.

to, in 1942, installing one of Frank Whittle's jet engines in the tail section of a Wellington. Should further information be required, Robert Gardiner's excellent book referred to below in the reference section is to be recommended. However, there is one wartime story concerning the development of Barnes Wallis's bouncing bomb that should not be omitted as it illustrates the point that the author has argued on many occasions, that often only one person receives credit for an invention that is in fact a team effort.

When George Edwards was growing up in Highams Park, his cousin Bob Gregory, a Surrey cricketer who had toured with England, taught the lad to play the game. The love of the sport remained with George for the rest of his life. Remarkably, the bowling skills George developed were to have a profound effect on German industry during the Second World War. When Barnes Wallace was experimenting with his bouncing bombs that were designed to destroy the hydroelectric dams of the Ruhr, he encountered problems concerning the height that the missile could bounce off the surface of the water. It was thought that the Germans had placed submarine nets across the dams to protect the massive walls, so it was important that the bombs could bounce high enough to clear these obstacles. There was also a requirement for the bombs to descend to a particular depth while hugging the dam wall, at which they could be detonated by a hydrostatic mechanism for maximum effect (see Chapter 5 of *From Gunpowder to Guns*, also in the Lea Valley Series).

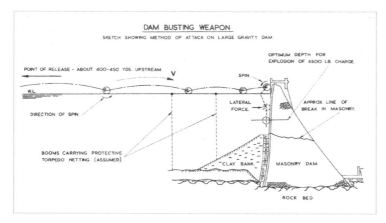

A diagram showing how Barnes Wallace's bouncing bomb was intended to breach the walls of the German hydroelectric dams in the Ruhr (courtesy of the RAF Museum). It was Sir George Edwards who suggested that backward spin be applied to the bomb before release from the aircraft. It was this inspired idea that kept the missile bouncing accurately and also allowed it to descend to the required depth by hugging the inside of the dam wall.

As Edwards' experimental department had designed the bomb's release mechanism from the aircraft, they were aware of the problems that Wallace was encountering. This is where Edwards' cricket knowledge came into play and he suggested to Wallace that the answer to the problem was to apply backward spin to the missile on release from the aircraft. Wallace was anything but convinced by the theoretical proposal, so Edwards had his team construct an experimental rig that could either apply no spin, topspin or backward spin to the missile. In February 1943 Wallace was invited to witness a demonstration that was to be carried out on Silvermere Lake in Surrey. First the missile was fired across the surface of the water with no spin applied and it just bounced four or five times. Then it was fired with topspin, which just made the missile go faster. On firing with back spin the missile skipped across the surface of the water achieving around fifteen bounces, totally vindicating Edwards' bowling theory. It is said that Wallace never gave Edwards credit for his contribution, although some years later he did suggest that the idea had come from a "county cricketer of my acquaintance".

On cessation of hostilities there was the expected fall-off in government work and the Vickers Company took the opportunity to reorganise. Barnes Wallace was moved to take charge of a new research department, the talented chief designer Rex Pierson was appointed overall chief engineer and George Edwards was made chief designer, working under Pierson. Sadly, soon after the reorganisation, Pierson became ill and in January 1948 he died, leaving Edwards with even greater responsibility.

Now back in the drawing office where his career had begun in 1935, Edwards would become not just one of the country's most innovative engineers and industrialists but an avid crusader for the whole of the post-war British aircraft industry. Apart from being responsible for the design and development of such famous aircraft as the Viking, the Varsity, the Valetta, the Viscount, the Vanguard, the Valiant (first 'V' bomber), the VC-10 and One Eleven, Edwards had the bitter disappointment, in 1955, of the government cancelling the development of the long-range military jet, the Vickers V 1000. This had the extremely serious knock-on effect of scuppering the civilian version, the VC7. Later Edwards was to express his frustration by describing the government decision as "the biggest blunder of all". The action had devastating consequences for the British aircraft industry as it offered the American aircraft manufacturers the long-range civil airline business on a plate. Edwards experienced another major disappoint in 1965 when the development programme for what had the potential to be the world's most advanced military aircraft, the TSR2, was cancelled.

A Vickers Viscount of Middle East Airlines in flight. This was one of the aircraft that Sir George Edwards had responsibility for designing. To impress potential buyers, one of the favourite tricks was to stand coins on edge on passenger dining tables to demonstrate the stability of the aircraft during flight.

Sir George Edwards, second from left, signing a contract with K.H. Staple of BOAC on 23 June 1960 to supply the company with ten Super VC10 aircraft.

A BOAC Super VC10 undergoing checks. Sir George Edwards had design and development responsibility for this aircraft.

Sir George Edwards, wearing a trilby hat, in deep conversation beneath the tail section of a BAC One-Eleven

Her Royal Highness the Duchess of Kent with Mr H. Matthey at Brimsdown after he had presented her with a platinum cigarette case (or possibly a powder compact), c.1949.

An incinerator used for burning material waste. This was a relatively new installation in c.2000.

Johnson & Matthey catalytic testing facilities at Royston, Hertfordshire.

Above: An operator pouring molten metal from a rotary converter at the Brimsdown plant, c.1948.

Left: An aerial view of the Johnson & Matthey Brimsdown plant, c.1930.

Far left: A Johnson & Matthey fine gold bar.

Left: A Johnson & Matthey platinum bar. This material has provided the electrical/electronic industries with excellent contacts for many years.

A recent aerial photograph of the Brimsdown plant, 2010.

Material brought from South Africa to Brimsdown in the 1950s to have valuable amounts of platinum group metals (pgms) extracted.

Nicky Gavron, the former Deputy Mayor of London, with a display version of a Johnson & Matthey Continuously Regenerating Trap (CRT).

The old smelting works at Brimsdown, c.1970. The wheeled vehicles in the foreground are cast-iron pots for collecting molten slag. These were humorously called "chariots" by the workforce.

Percival Norton Johnson FRS and George Matthey.

Platinum group metals (pgms) dissolution plant at Brimsdown, c.2000.

The newly constructed Johnson & Matthey factory at Brimsdown, September 1950, looking south across Mossops Creek.

Selling jewellery in Beijing made from Johnson & Matthey platinum. This is a sign of China becoming one of the world's most affluent societies.

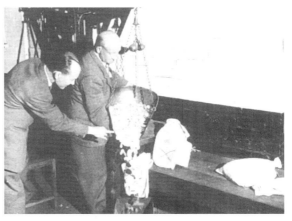

Weighing Saudi Arabian gold coins at Brimsdown in the 1950s.

independent business.

The Johnson Matthey Company today is a far cry from the modest business that started in Maiden Lane. In the highly competitive industrial world in which we live, there is a constant need to monitor, not only the internal technologies and processes of the manufacturing plant, but the ever-changing needs of our planet. In recent years Johnson Matthey has successfully carried out a major programme to change the focus of the group's activities and has invested heavily in the design, development and manufacture of a number of environmentally friendly products. The company is now a world leader in design and manufacture of emission-control systems (auto catalysts) for cars, motorcycles, heavy-duty diesel trucks and buses. Pioneering work by Johnson Matthey on fuel cells, a new source of power by converting energy from a chemical reaction into electricity, is set to revolutionise our homes and the vehicles we drive by ridding our cities of toxic emissions. In a world where mineral and other resources are becoming scarcer by the day, Johnson Matthey is performing a valuable service by recovering precious metals, not only from a diversity of ores, but from a range of waste materials returned to Brimsdown. The waste comes in all forms, both wet and dry, and is the residue of many manufacturing processes from across the globe. Constantly developing more efficient procedures to recover and process platinum group metals (pgms) has made Johnson Matthey the largest fabricator in this field in the world. It would require several books to chart all the achievements and international progress of Johnson Matthey with manufacturing facilities, offices, partnerships and agents in almost every country, the like of which John Johnson could never have contemplated in 1762.

REFERENCES

Annual Report & Accounts 2000, Johnson Matthey

Assay, Magazine of the Johnson Matthey Group, Johnson Matthey, 2000

McDonald, Donald, *Percival Norton Johnson*, Johnson Matthey & Co. Limited, 1951

McDonald, Donald, *A History of Platinum*, Johnson Matthey & Co. Limited, 1961

McDonald, Donald, *The Johnsons of Maiden Lane*, Johnson Matthey & Co. Limited, 1964

Note

The author would like to acknowledge the help and assistance given by Mike Rhead (former Operations Manager of Johnson Matthey, Brimsdown), Barry Connoly (current Site Manager of Johnson Matthey, Brimsdown) and Ian Godwin (Director – Investor Relations & Corporate) for providing information on the company and also for arranging a conducted tour of the plant.

4. ALLEN AND HANBURYS OF WARE

Like so many Lea Valley stories, the one of Allen and Hanburys of Ware has its founding origins elsewhere; and also like other Lea Valley stories, the association of this company with prominent names in history is truly remarkable.

In December 1715 a twenty-four-year-old apothecary, Silvanus Bevan, took the lease of a shop in Old Plough Court, off London's Lombard Street, to commence his business. Bevan, a Quaker, had leased the premises from Salem Osgood, also a Quaker, and it is these religious and moral connections that permeate the early years of the business. It seems to be the case, as evidenced by these early transactions, that Quakers preferred to do business and also to associate with those who shared a common belief and moral code. Also it should be remembered that, at the time and because of their religious beliefs, Quakers did not have the same civic freedoms as others in the community.

The home of Luke Howard when he lived in Balaam Street, Plaistow, now part of the Greater London Borough of Newham.

On the death of Silvanus in 1786 the business eventually passed down through the Bevan family line until it reached Joseph, who in 1792 took on William Allen as a confidential clerk. By 1794, with failing health, Joseph retired from the business and took up an interest in writing, later becoming a successful author. He was succeeded by Samuel Mildred, the son of a partner in the pharmaceutical firm of Mildred & Roberts. In 1795 Mildred took on Joseph Bevan's clerk William Allen as a partner, the firm becoming Mildred & Allen. Two years later in 1797, Mildred retired and sold his share of the business to Allen for £525. Soon after completing the transaction, Allen took on Luke Howard, a Quaker friend, as a partner and the firm became Allen and Howard.

Luke Howard's father, Robert, a successful manufacturer of iron and tin products, had given his son a good start in life with an education at a private school in Oxfordshire. After leaving school at fourteen

An early engraving of Plough Court in the City of London.

Timothy Bevan (1704–1786)

William Allen FRS (1770–1843)

he served an apprenticeship with a retail chemist at Stockport. On completion of his training in 1773 at the age of twenty-one, Howard set up in business as a chemist at an address near London's Temple Bar.

After joining in partnership with Allen in 1797, Howard established a manufacturing laboratory at Plaistow, then a small village in east London, now part of the borough of Newham. Here he remained running the business until the partnership dissolved in 1805. Howard then moved to City Mills, Stratford and set up in his own right as Howard & Sons. The business remained at Stratford until it was moved to Ilford, Essex in 1914. While at Plaistow, Howard became interested in meteorology and later gave cloud formations the names still used today, so he is much more renowned as the father of modern meteorology than as an early industrial chemist.

After Howard had left the business, Allen took on John Thomas Barry who later took over the running of the Plaistow manufacturing laboratory, eventually becoming a partner in the firm which then became William Allen & Company. In the year 1808 we first see the name of Hanbury appear when Daniel Bell Hanbury entered Plough Court. By 1856, through a succession of family members joining the firm, the more familiar name of Allen &

Cornelius Hanbury (1827–1916)   Daniel Hanbury (1825–1875)

Hanburys comes into being. Within four years the firm was establishing itself overseas with a cod liver oil factory in Newfoundland and by the time of the Great War more factories had opened, five in Norway and a further two in Britain. By 1878, a new factory was opened in Bethnal Green, east London and between 1800 and 1805 a forge, for making surgical instruments, was added to the plant. Skilled instrument makers from Sheffield were brought in to run the new forge.

With a view to expanding the overseas markets, in 1884 F. Forest & Company of Melbourne were appointed agents for Australia and in 1894 Reddick & Company (East India Merchants) were given responsibility for representing the firm in India and a depot was opened in Calcutta. In Britain, a pharmacy was opened in London's affluent Vere Street to ensure contact was established with the West End medical community and later, in 1894, a workshop and showroom was opened in Wigmore Street.

The year 1896 saw Allen & Hanbury acquire the now familiar mill site at Ware, the start of a successful, and continuing, long-term association with the Hertfordshire town. Two years later, in 1898, the town's site at Buryfield was acquired for a new factory for production of foods and malt products. In the same year, overseas expansion continued apace with agencies being established in Canada and the United States of America. As the twentieth century dawned, inroads into the South African pharmaceutical market were made with depots being established in Cape Town and Durban. South America became the next target with the formation of a subsidiary company in Buenos Aires. In 1912 a plant was established in Moscow although this was short lived, being taken over by the Bolsheviks in 1917.

Bottled malt products at Ware waiting to be boxed.

A display of Allen and Hanburys surgical equipment at the Manchester Surgical Exhibition of 1927.

The Allen and Hanburys
steam vehicle fleet at the start
of the twentieth century. It
took five hours for one of
these lorries to travel from
Ware to their London factory
at Bethnal Green.

Allen and Hanburys' Bethnal
Green factory as it would
have looked in the late
nineteenth century.

The Allen and Hanburys
transport fleet, c.1920.
Presumably the travelling
time from Ware to London
has been shortened as the
fleet is equipped with vans
employing internal
combustion engines.

Building workers who were employed to make improvements
to the Allen and Hanburys Ware Mill, c.1900.

Drug grinding, stamping and sieving machinery that was once
employed at Ware. The edge runner mill in the picture is similar to
the ones that were used in the manufacture of gunpowder at the
Royal Gunpowder Mills, Waltham Abbey.

An early evaporating vessel
that was once employed at
the Ware factory.

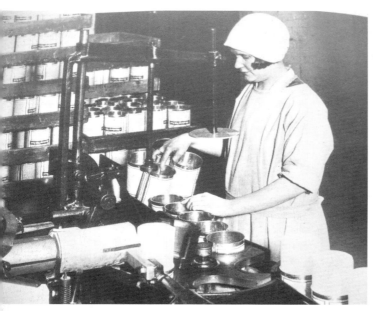

Unpacking a straw-filled crate outside Plough Court, c.1886.

A woman operative preparing food cans at Ware in the 1930s.

The head pond at Ware Mill c.1910.

A view of the Allen and Hanburys factory buildings at Ware in 1947.

During the Second World War enemy bombing severely damaged the Bethnal Green factory and production was transferred away from the London site to the safer facilities at Ware. The Plough Court premises also sustained considerable damage and Allen & Hanburys eventually vacated the site, bringing to an end a direct link with their historic roots. However, the early forays into international initiatives and acquisitions had established Allen & Hanburys across the world as a major supplier of pharmaceutical products. The on-going development of successful ranges of drugs and medicines and specialist foods have contributed greatly to the British economy and over the years provided employment for thousands of people.

In 1958, Glaxo Laboratories Limited, a company that can trace its history back to 1873 when Joseph Nathan established a general trading business, Joseph Nathan and Company at Wellington, New Zealand, acquired Allen & Hanburys. The next twenty years saw a vast expansion of the business through the setting up of new factories in the United Kingdom and the merging of activities at Greenford and Ware, to become Glaxo Group Research Limited. Dr David Jack, formerly responsible for research within the company, was appointed Chairman and Chief Executive, later becoming a Director of Glaxo Group Limited.

The 1980s saw company fortunes rise yet again with a range of tried and tested medicines and drugs like Ventolin, developed at Ware, and Zantac reaching record sales especially on the export market. None of these successes could have come about without massive investment in research and development. Nevertheless, it must be remembered that all scientific research to find treatments and cures for some of the world's most challenging diseases such as cancer and AIDS can take decades to perfect and successful solutions are often difficult to find.

If we think back to the generation before we will soon realise that we are, on average, living longer than our parents and our quality of life has been greatly enhanced by the medicines and drugs that are currently available to us. These health-enhancing breakthroughs

The restored Allen and Hanburys building in Priory Street, Ware (2010).

have been achieved by armies of scientists around the world working continually to solve complex problems which on occasion, because of limits of the technology available, can turn out to be insurmountable in a particular epoch, and we have to wait for future success. However, scientists could never have achieved any of their goals without the teamwork of engineers and architects who developed the plant, designed the machinery and buildings that allowed the pharmaceutical business to manufacture and process the drugs, medicines and specialist foods in the scrupulously hygienic way that is demanded by modern legislation. William Allen in his Plough Court days could never in his wildest dreams have imagined the standards of cleanliness and sterility that are currently being achieved by the world's leading pharmaceutical manufacturers.

A 2010 aerial photograph of the main GSK factory complex at Ware.

The GSK research pharmacy building at Ware which opened in 1989.

By 1995, Glaxo had merged with another world leader in the pharmaceutical industry, Wellcome, forming the company Glaxo Wellcome. In the same year Her Majesty the Queen opened the new Glaxo Wellcome Medicines Research Centre at Stevenage, Hertfordshire. Wellcome had come into existence in 1880 when Henry Wellcome, a salesman for a leading American pharmaceutical business, was persuaded to come to London and form a partnership with a friend, Silas Burrows, a former Philadelphia pharmacist, who

GSK House, the headquarters of the company at Brentford, Middlesex.

had established a trading company in the United Kingdom, the business becoming Burrows Wellcome & Company. When Burrows died, Wellcome continued growing the business and became very wealthy, allowing him to pursue one of his childhood interests, the history of mankind. In 1913 he founded the Wellcome Historical Medical Museum and throughout his life added to the collection, although many artefacts he acquired were never displayed. In 1976 the Wellcome Trust came to an agreement with the Science Museum and the collection of some 114,000 items was transferred to this establishment on permanent loan.

The next milestone in the fortunes of Glaxo Wellcome occurred on 27 December 2000 when they merged with another major industry company, Smith Kline Beecham, to form Glaxo Smith Kline (GSK). Like many pharmaceutical companies that had arrived at the new millennium, Smith Kline Beecham had its roots in the nineteenth century and in its own right had gone through numerous mergers and acquisitions, finally merging their respective businesses in 1989.

Mrs and Mr
Charles Kingston
Welch

source while he kept a steady hand on the cutting tool during the shaping process. Welch's mould was constructed out of hard wood that he had accurately shaped to follow the outer circumference of a thirty-inch tyre cover and the mould was then divided into four hinged sections to allow easy removal of the tyre when the moulding process was complete.

The next obstacle to overcome, once the mould was completed, was to make the first 'extensible' edge tyre cover and, in the words of Fred, "what a sticky messy job that was". Charles first tried to form the tyre cover on his workshop bench but he found the surface too rough and splintery. Like many early designers, each time he encountered a problem he had to come up with a simple practical solution if his project were going to progress. Expensive purpose-built equipment was not an option. In this case, Charles managed to acquire a polished top from an old harpsichord and this proved ideal for the job.

The following is a brief description by Fred of how he and his brother formed the first experimental tyres:

> Dimensional strips of lining fabric were laid out on the polished surface and coated with rubber solution. When sufficiently dry they were stretched over the mould; the edging wires were pressed over a projecting flange of the mould, the edges of the fabric were then drawn up over the wire forming a pocket in which the wires were retained in position; finally the rubber covering was solutioned [sic] and stuck over the fabric lining.

The locking pin was withdrawn from the mould and the first Welch's patent tyre was complete.

Unfortunately, Fred ends his article with the tyre-forming description and we are left in the dark as to how many tyres the brothers produced using this rather crude method. It would also have been helpful to know if Charles found another India-rubber manufacturer to make his samples, or did he expect the company who would finally buy his idea to seek out a producer?

In 1891, Welch sold his patent to the Dunlop Company, which agreed to pay £5,000 for the British and Belgian rights, £1,000 for the French and a further £1,500 for the American. Returning to the earlier-mentioned 'what if' question, had William Warne and Company, the Tottenham India-rubber manufacturers, not been so hasty in rejecting Welch's invention, think of the world-wide business they could have had! When Welch originally took his sample tyre to them he also made the company a generous offer that would have allowed Warne to become the sole concessionaire. Had this manufacturer persevered a little longer with Welch's sample to overcome the production difficulties and been more accommodating, it could well be that the name of Warne, rather than Dunlop, would be associated with the world of tyres today and Charles Kingston Welch would not have remained in relative obscurity as the largely forgotten inventor of the wires in the tyre.

REFERENCES

Cook, Jim, *John Boyd Dunlop*, Dreoilin Specialist Publications Limited, County Meath, Ireland, 2000

Du Cros, Arthur, *Wheels of Fortune*, Chapman & Hall, London, 1938

Glynn, Francis, *History of the Clincher Tyre and Rim*, North British Rubber Company Limited, Edinburgh, 1900

Grew, W.F., *The Cycle Industry*, Pitman Press, London, 1921

Welch, Fred, 'Why Wires in Tyres?', *Cycling Magazine*, 5 February 1958

Note

The author is indebted to Don Ellis of the Veteran Cycle Club for generously making available his collection of research notes on Charles Kingston Welch to assist the writing of this chapter which has helped to resurrect the name of Tottenham's unsung hero. I am also indebted to the writer and journalist, Ms Julie Welch, the great niece of Charles Kingston Welch, for information about her great uncle and for making several illustrations available to support this chapter.

6. W. WILLIAMSON, THE LOST LAUNDRY ENGINEERS OF HACKNEY

The nineteenth-century laundry engineering company W. Williamson has been one of the most elusive Lea Valley firms that I have had to research so far. This story started with what appeared to be a casual enquiry for information; but on this occasion, things turned out to be a little different. Normally I receive enquiries about Lea Valley industries from within the UK but this particular request had come from Simon's Town, South Africa.

The person who contacted me was a David Erickson, a member of the Simon's Town Historical Society, who, with colleagues, had been carrying out a survey of the former Royal Naval Hospital that was once part of the Simon's Town Naval base. During the survey, the members had discovered an almost intact suite of laundry machinery complete with overhead line shafting, brackets and extractor fan. What had caught their eyes was the name of the manufacturer, boldly embossed on the various machines and brackets: "W. Williamson & Co. Ltd., Milborne Works, Well Street, London NE". This information quickly raised the level of enquiry

A 1906 plan showing the layout of the Royal Navy Hospital, Simon's Town, South Africa.

Map of South Africa. Simon's Town is located slightly to the left of the centre of False Bay.

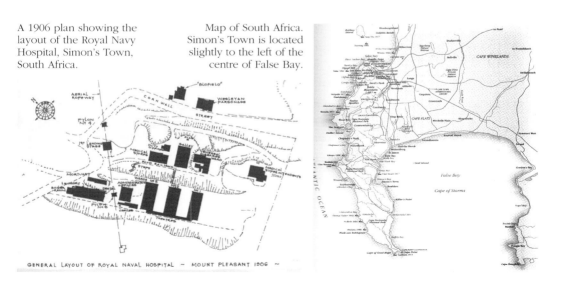

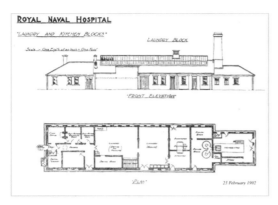

A plan of the Royal Navy
Hospital, Simon's Town, 1902.

A view of the Simon's Town Dockyard
through the dock gates.

The name of W. Williamson boldly displayed
on equipment in the laundry.

A general view of Simon's Town. The Navy
Dockyard is towards the left of the picture.

The Simon's Town Museum, currently run by
volunteers from the local historical society.

The Simon's Town Dockyard and Marina with ships of the South African Navy in the background and smaller craft in the foreground.

A piece of Williamson laundry equipment. Note the line-shafting pulleys to the top right.

This picture shows four pieces of Williamson laundry equipment still in place along with an almost intact line-shafting system.

The Royal Navy Simon's Town laundry block as it appears today (2010).

A well-preserved Williamson line-shafting wall bracket.

A Williamson extractor fan that would have been belt driven from a pulley on the line shafting.

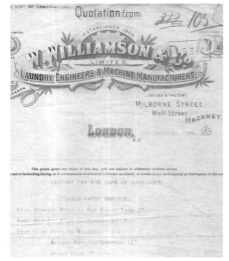

A Williamson letter dated 3 October 1900 showing "established 1850" on the letterhead.

An embossed metal plate clearly showing the Hackney address of the Williamson Company.

and information was sought to discover the company's origins. As I am known for my love of the Lea Valley region, the request ended up in my email inbox. Having received such clear information regarding the company address, I thought my research would be relatively easy. This, as it turned out, was not the case.

My obvious starting point was the Hackney Archives Department and I was able to confirm, through a reference in the 1900–1 Hackney and Homerton directory, that W. Williamson & Co. Ltd., were located on the west side of Milborne Street. A street number for the address was not given but the company was listed after number eleven, the last number recorded for that side of the street. This was the only clue to the company's existence as the trade directories either side of the 1900-1 date did not list the name of W. Williamson. At first sight, such information might suggest that the company was only in existence for a few years but this would be the wrong assumption to make. It is not unknown, perhaps due to financial circumstances, for a company not to pay the annual fee and therefore to be excluded from the trade directory listings.

Experience has shown that certain records often turn up in a neighbouring borough's archive but this was not the case when I checked. Further checks were carried out with the National Archive, the London Metropolitan Archive and the Bishopsgate Institute, all to no avail. However, an email enquiry to the London Guildhall Library did produce a little more information and I was fortunate to receive the following reply:

> The firm is listed in Kelly's *Directories of merchants, manufacturers and shippers* as well as the *Post Office London* directories. The company first appears in these directories in 1891 as Williamson Welburn & Co., 133 High Holborn, WC and remained at this address until 1896. In 1897 the firm became W. Williamson & Co., 2 White Horse Buildings, 100 High Holborn, WC and Milborne Works, Hackney and is described as supplying complete plants for steam and hand laundries. W. Williamson & Co. became a limited liability company in 1899 and moved from High Holborn to Milborne Street, Well Street, Hackney NE. It remained in business until 1902 when it seems to have gone into voluntary liquidation, (*London Gazette*, 2 and 9 May 1902).
>
> In the 1901–2 *Post Office London* directories, the firm is described as makers of "Williamson" washing machines, hydros, drying closets, ironing machines, mangles. Contractors to H.M. Admiralty & H.M. War Office.

While the information from the Guildhall Library explained why an entry for W. Williamson did not appear in the local Hackney and Homerton directory after 1901, I was still left without knowledge of the origins of the company and had yet to discover anything substantial about the founders.

As the sources of likely information seemed to be running out, the opportunity to appeal to the residents of Hackney through a local newspaper seemed to be worth taking. The reason behind this initiative was to discover if any Williamson descendants were living locally or if perhaps there was someone who may have had relatives that had once worked for the company. The editor of the *Hackney Gazette* was duly contacted and when it was explained that we seemed to know more about the ancient Egyptians and Greeks than we did about a local nineteenth-century engineering company, he readily agreed to run an appeal for information. An article appeared in the 26 November 2009 issue of the newspaper and, perhaps unsurprisingly, given the scarcity of information to date, not a single response was forthcoming.

In an almost last-ditch attempt to discover something about the company, research was carried out at the Institution of Mechanical Engineers (IMechE) in case W. Williamson had been a member of this body. Unfortunately this too proved to be another dead end, although the time at the Institution was not totally wasted. While searching the IMechE archive I came across the name Edward Williamson and it was thought this required further investigation. As it turned out, Edward was elected an Associate Member of the IMechE in 1889 at the age of 38, transferring to Member in 1921 and, from his biographical details, recorded in the memoirs of the Institution, we learn a little of his engineering background.

Edward gained his early training from 1877 to 1883 in his father's factory under the tutelage of his uncle C.B. Williamson, an engineer who manufactured woodworking and other machinery. After completing his training he was appointed assistant manager at a firm in High Holborn that was owned by another uncle. In 1890 Edward subsequently moved to W. Williamson in Hackney where he became managing director, a position he maintained until 1902. This is the year when the Guildhall records show that W. Williamson went into voluntary liquidation. So, to have a better understanding of what had happened to the business, more research will be required. Perhaps a reader will feel sufficiently encouraged to take up the challenge, and, if the gauntlet is picked up, I would be delighted to learn the outcome.

The year 1902 appears to have been an eventful one for Edward as almost immediately after he departed W. Williamson he took the position of engineering representative with Manlove, Alliott and Company Limited of Nottingham. Referring to the memoir we learn that Edward was appointed London manager to the Nottingham firm in 1913 and his job clearly carried considerable responsibility. As the memoir states, "He was personally responsible for the installation of boilers, pumps and laundry machinery at the Royal Naval hospitals at Chatham and Haslar, the King Edward Memorial Hospital at Lahore, the West Suffolk Hospital, the Royal Air Force Station at Cranwell as well as for other many important contracts: he was also responsible for the fitting of oil fuel galleys for *HMS Hood* and other vessels." Edward retired from Manlove, Alliott and Company Limited in 1936 after spending thirty-four years at the firm. He died in his eighty-first year at his Hurlingham home on 6 November 1940.

Until further research is carried out we might wish to speculate why it was decided that the firm of W. Williamson should go into voluntary liquidation so soon after supplying the Simon's Town Royal Naval base with laundry equipment. Edward, as managing director at the time, would have been a key player in the decision-making process to close the Hackney business. Directly after this he took a responsible position in a company which appears, due to its product range, to have been a competitor of Williamson, so one might conclude that Edward had already established a good business-like relationship with his new employer, hence the swift move in 1902. It is possible that Manlove, Alliott and Company were former suppliers of sub-contracted machine parts to Williamson and this business link would have allowed Edward to have built up a strong working relationship. Perhaps after supplying the Simon's Town Royal Naval base with laundry equipment new contracts were slow to materialise for the Hackney Company thereby prompting Edward to take the opportunity to close the business and join a competitor for an easier life. Unless further research turns up more information about W. Williamson of Hackney, maybe we will never know.

I believe that it is crucially important to record the story of W. Williamson, albeit incomplete, before it is lost forever. It is probably fair to conclude that other historians of the Lea Valley's industrial archaeology and elsewhere will be able to recount similar research experiences. This story is just another example of a manufacturer, which made a significant contribution to the world that we live in, almost escaping the scene before being properly recorded, probably due to someone making the decision to incinerate company records without first referring to a local museum or archive.

The Royal Navy first operated from the base at Simon's Town in the late eighteenth century and then again in 1806, and Simon's Town became the home of the South Atlantic Squadron. When Napoleon Bonaparte was exiled to St Helena it was the role of that Squadron to provide supplies and security to the South Atlantic outpost, some 1,200 miles away from Simon's Town, until his death in 1821.

The South Atlantic Squadron also played a significant role in enforcing the abolition of the slave trade, patrolling vast distances of ocean from Sierra Leone on the West Coast to Mombassa on the East Coast of Africa along with the islands of Seychelles and Mauritius to make sure that ships were not carrying illegal cargoes. Also the Simon's Town Royal Navy base played a crucial role in keeping southern hemisphere trade routes safe before the opening of the Suez Canal in November 1869.

During the First and Second World Wars, the Royal Navy operating from the base played an important role in escorting troop convoys that were en route to Europe from Australia, New Zealand and the Far East, while the dockyards of Simon's Town repaired and gave shelter to many ships.

The naval authorities had commissioned the building of a new hospital on the slopes of Cable Hill, Simon's Town to replace an earlier hospital that had once stood in the middle of the town. Construction of the new facilities took place between 1901 and 1904. At the northern end of the site an additional building was added that housed a dental surgery, an incinerator for burning medical waste and a laundry and it was here that the Hackney machinery was installed. The Royal Navy hospital was officially opened on 11 October 1904 by Princess Christian of Schleswig-Holstein, the third daughter of Queen Victoria and for over fifty years the Hackney-built machinery served the Royal Navy until the Simon's Town base was handed over to the South African Navy in 1957.

Today the main hospital block has been transformed for a range of different uses, but the laundry building with the majority of its machinery remains intact. The Simon's Town Historical Society currently has ideas of bringing the laundry back to life as an example of late Victorian machinery in operation. If they are successful in their quest, it would be a fitting legacy to a Lea Valley company that had sent quality equipment to the other side of the world.

REFERENCES

Author unknown, *Simon's Town, its History*, Simon's Town Historical Society

Correspondence between the author and David Erickson and Professor Boet Dommisse of the Simon's Town Historical Society, 2009–10

Note

A copy of a W. Williamson & Co. letter, dated 3 October 1900, was sent to the author by the Simon's Town Historical Society. The letter was part of a quotation for the supply of laundry equipment to the Royal Navy and an interesting clue to the company's establishment appeared on the letterhead – "established 1850" – suggesting that the company had been in existence for fifty years. When the company finally closed in 1902 the total would have been fifty-two years.

7. FROM MONKS TO MODERNITY – NEWHAM'S CONTINUING PROGRESSION

Looking at Stratford today it is almost impossible to imagine that the area was once open marshland stretching towards the Thames. It is probably even more difficult to imagine a group of Cistercian monks building a monastery here. The monastery, begun in the twelfth century, was to become known as the Abbey of Stratford Langthorne or, more familiarly, West Ham Abbey.

Abbot Robert, who had become increasingly uncomfortable with the growing wealth and power of the Benedictines, led twenty-one monks away from his monastery at Molesmes in France and founded the Cistercian order in 1098 at Citeaux, east of Dijon. Although scholars have differed with regard to the figures, it would seem that within one hundred years of founding their order the Cistercians had established around eight hundred abbeys across Europe. Research has shown that the order established their communities near fertile ground usually away from areas of high population. This would suggest that, at the time when West Ham Abbey was being built, Stratford was a relatively isolated and sparsely populated place. The Domesday survey of 1086 tells us that the population of the area, which later became known as West Ham, comprised forty-eight villagers, seventy-nine smallholders and three slaves.

After studying ancient Abbey leases, the nineteenth-century historian Katharine Fry was able to construct this map. From her researches she was able to predict the approximate location of several Abbey buildings and structures. However, later archaeology would suggest that not all her predictions were completely accurate.

From old maps and documents it can be deduced that the Abbey occupied a site of approximately twenty acres and was situated east of the Channelsea River and west of Manor Road (formerly Marsh Lane). Travellers approaching London from the east could not have failed to see what must have been a massive building

Saint Bernard of Clairvaux (1090–1153), a French abbot said to have been responsible for reforming the Cistercian order.

silhouetted against the skyline. By the time of the dissolution of the monasteries between 1536 and 1540 by Henry VIII, the site had grown to accommodate mills, kilns, orchards, gardens, moated areas, a tanning house, a slaughterhouse, a bake house, a church and various other buildings. So it can be seen that, over the years, the monks had created a self-sustaining community. To accomplish this level of self-sufficiency the Cistercians had developed a sound economic model to ensure that the day-to-day tasks of running the monastery were carried out efficiently. This was achieved by creating a two-tier system of monks and in today's terminology it would probably be classified as a division of labour. Lay brothers were admitted to the monastery but they were not required to carry out spiritual functions. Their duties were purely the management and running of the agricultural, commercial and industrial side of the community.

Originally the Cistercians had begun their order to get away from what they perceived as the greed and wealth of the Benedictines and in the beginning they endured a way of life that was based upon strict self-discipline and denial. They chose to wear simple clothes, to sleep on beds of straw and to keep to a diet which, in the main, excluded fish and animal

The West Ham coat of arms, the design of which has been heavily influenced by symbols associated with the Cistercian order at Stratford Langthorne Abbey. Note the chevrons and crosier.

products. However, it would seem that their strict regime was relatively short-lived and the order appears to have returned to a more material way of life similar to that originally shunned by their breakaway brethren.

In about 1134, William de Montfichet, a French baron residing in England, acting on the advice of the Archbishop of Canterbury, pledged by charter that:

> I have given in alms to the Church of God, and St. Mary, and all saints of Ham, and the abbot and monks there serving God, all my demesne of Ham, in land, in arable fields, in meadows, in marsh, in water, and especially all the land, which was Ranulph's the priest. And besides the meadow in my demesne, the eleven acres, which I exchanged with Gerald de Ham for fourteen acres of land in the marsh, and two mills near the Stratford causeway, namely one held by Ulwin the miller, and my wood of Bocherst and the tithe of my pannage at… pasture…

A woodcut by Katherine Fry showing, what was thought to be, one of the arches of the Abbey cloister. This was one of the parts of the Abbey that had been built into the wall of the former Adam and Eve public house.

William de Montfichet granted a further charter to the Abbot and Convent of Stratford allowing them "the gifts of his feudal tenants". However, at the time, ancient common law did not allow religious communities to hold land without receiving Royal confirmation. Henry II granted this to the monks of Stratford in 1182. The Stratford monks became even more powerful as, over the years, they received further privileges. Richard Coeur de Lion alone granted them two further charters, which extended the land they held far beyond the original boundaries of the Abbey.

If we possessed the ability to be whisked back in time to an early Stratford, we may have caught glimpses of monks walking solemnly through the Abbey cloisters deep in prayer while others meditated. Some might be seen tending the Abbey gardens and orchards while others, we might assume, discussed the

The Adam and Eve public house that once stood in Abbey Road. Note the stonework around the window to the left of the door. This was said to have been 'robbed' from the ruins of Stratford Langthorne Abbey.

The Caernarfon window, taken from the Adam and Eve public house, and now installed in the porch of West Ham Church. This helps to remind us that the church was once part of the Stratford Langthorne Abbey complex.

scientific and technical problems of the day. In recent years, leading researchers have agreed that the Cistercians were highly competent engineers. Close examination of some of the remaining abbeys across Europe has led to the conclusion that the order was capable of achieving quite astonishing feats of engineering, particularly in the building of complex structures and also in the construction of water channels.

It is not absolutely clear what happened to the Abbey lands at the time of dissolution, but by the early 1730s changes were occurring to the site at Stratford Langthorne that would begin the process of removing the final remnants of the ancient buildings from public view forever. When the first Adam and Eve public house (now demolished) was built within the Abbey grounds, part of what was thought to have been an arch of the cloister was incorporated into the building's wall. Later, in 1784, land adjacent to the Adam and Eve was purchased by Thomas Holbrook, a brewer, who then dug up much of the remaining ruins for use as building material and also for sale. By the nineteenth century, to support the growing population and the expanding economy, developers, civil engineers and builders finished off the vandalism and demolition work that Henry VIII, Thomas Holbrook and others had started. In the 1840s,

A funerary stone that was unearthed from the site of Stratford Langthorne Abbey. The stone is now set into an internal wall, below the tower, of West Ham Church.

the construction of the North Woolwich Railway cut a large swathe through the site and, in the 1870s, more alterations occurred when the railway was widened. In the 1860s a large part of the site was taken over for a massive civil engineering scheme, the building of Bazalgette's northern outfall sewer. These projects altered considerably the topography of the Abbey precincts.

The local historian Katharine Fry (1801–86), daughter of the famous prison reformer Elizabeth, described what she saw as she travelled through the area of Stratford Langthorne in the latter half of the nineteenth century. Katharine, who was meticulous about detail, had constructed a map from information obtained from old leases to show, as best she could, where some of the Abbey structures had originally been located. She began her journey near All Saints Church, West Ham and proceeded along Abbey Road towards the Channelsea River. Her journey took her past the Leather Cloth Factory, which she explained was on her left hand side and built on the site of the old parish workhouse. Some fifty yards on (probably near Baker's Row today), she suggested, was the site of the great arched gate of the Abbey (the line of Abbey Road would have passed through it). In her narrative, Katharine explains that the road ran parallel to a ditch that formed part of the moat, which once surrounded the Abbey grounds. On the inner side of the moat, she suggests, was a site originally occupied by two gardens. Katharine concluded that the monk porter, who had the responsibility of looking after the great gate, would have also tended these.

A drawing of All Saints Church, West Ham, c.1830, looking east down Church Street.

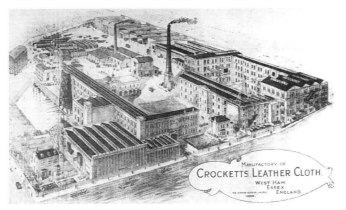

Crocketts Leather Cloth Factory, once located in Abbey Road, West Ham and mentioned by Katherine Fry on her walk from All Saints Church towards the ruins of the Abbey. The factory closed in 1961 and was demolished c.1962.

A white stone arch filled in with red brick, from a woodcut by Katherine Fry. Thought to be the possible entrance to the monastery from the grange or farmyard.

A drawing of a damaged seal with incomplete wording 'Sigill com… Stratforde'.

The great gate of Stratford Langthorne Abbey that would have once straddled the line of the present Abbey Road, from a mid-eighteenth-century engraving.

From the various leases that Katharine had examined she had cleverly worked out the approximate location of several Abbey buildings and, in particular, the possible position of the slaughterhouse. This building had apparently stood near to a barn of a moated house and she has included this structure, along with other site detail, on her map. It would take too much space to reproduce all Katharine's researches here, but there is one further description that will be of particular interest to the industrial historian. Apart from her clarity of writing, Katharine Fry had a wonderful eye for detail and she used this gift to produce excellent drawings and woodcuts of the things she observed. She describes her picture of the Abbey Mills "as seen from the marshes" as:

> an accurate representation of them as they were in the year 1830, surrounded by the ancient willows, which grew amongst the ditches, and were believed to have been planted by the monks. Of these mills in their ancient condition, nothing now remains.

Although the monastery had been dissolved in the sixteenth century, it would appear that milling had continued to at least the early part of the nineteenth century. Later maps of this period show a single mill, called Abbey Mill, located on the Channelsea River, complete with head and tail streams, at a point where Abbey Road turns north sharply to meet Abbey Lane. Coincidentally, while researching the mills at Stratford, I had the good fortune to meet a

A late-eighteenth-century engraving of a slightly altered Abbey Mills as compared to the Katherine Fry drawing. Also the artist appears to have been positioned differently.

Katherine Fry's drawing of the Abbey Mills which she claims "is an accurate representation of them as they were in the year 1830".

Miss Marjorie Cox, who told the author that her great, great, great, great grandfather, Hanson Flight (1737–1823) was the miller of Abbey Mills. The photograph was taken in the garden of Miss Cox's flat within the Alms Houses of the Worshipful Company of Weavers.

Miss Marjorie Cox who told me that her great, great, great, great grandfather, Hanson Flight (1737-1823) was the miller of Abbey Mills. It is claimed that apart from Abbey Mills supplying large quantities of flour to the bakeries of London, they also kept Wellington's army supplied during the Peninsular Wars.

Hanson's son Joseph (1773-1811) followed his father as the miller of Abbey Mills. The Post Office Annual Directory of 1811 lists 'Flight & Co., Mealmen, Stratford'. Unfortunately Joseph met with a tragic death on 2 February 1811 when he was only thirty-eight. On his way home to Stratford, thieves set upon him as he crossed Bow Bridge. Joseph was thrown from his horse and left to drown in the River Lea.

A further interesting fact about the Flight family is that in 1783 Hanson's older brother Thomas (1726–1800) bought the Worcester Porcelain Company for his sons John and Joseph. In 1788, after a visit from George III, Thomas was granted the Royal Warrant.

Sadly, the only reminders today that Stratford once supported a thriving Cistercian community where cowled monks in long robes went about their daily tasks are place names like Abbey Lane, Abbey Road and the Abbey Mills Pumping Station of Thames Water. However, it is possible that, like Miss Cox, others, with sufficient time and patience, could trace their ancestry back to an earlier period, perhaps to the Normans. While carrying out this research it is possible that other interesting facts will come to light that will help us improve our knowledge of Stratford Langthorne Abbey.

Fortunately, in 1983, British Rail engineers, when working on the electrification of the North Woolwich Railway, made a chance discovery of two skeletons on the former Stratford Langthorne Abbey site. The rail authorities alerted the Passmore Edwards Museum and under the direction of Ms Pat Wilkinson an archaeological dig was carried out. After several months' work, around one hundred and thirty skeletons were discovered suggesting that this must have been the site of the Abbey cemetery. Later, between 1991 and 1994, when work was being carried out on the Jubilee Line extension, the Newham Museum Service and the Oxford Archaeological Unit completed archaeological excavations. This work uncovered the remains of a number of buildings within the Abbey precincts and some six hundred and eighty three skeletons were found in what was thought to be the Abbey cemetery. The skeletal remains were removed and reburied at Mount St. Bernard Abbey, Leicestershire.

Archaeological excavations at the Stratford Langthorne Abbey site in October 1983.

The story of Stratford Langthorne Abbey illustrates one of many chapters in the incredibly rich history of Newham. Although relatively little physical evidence remains, it does however illustrate that while we can only see the current new development this would not have been possible without the establishment of the community by earlier people.

NEWHAM'S INNOVATIVE PAST

Earlier books in the Lea Valley series have recorded many scientific and engineering achievements that occurred in and around Newham and also told the stories of the entrepreneurs who were responsible for these developments. It seems appropriate, therefore, in a book that largely deals with regeneration, to remind readers of some of these earlier events and also the people that created the blueprint that helped shape our modern world.

The nineteenth century was an age of great change and much innovation as inventors, engineers and entrepreneurs came together to meet the challenges created by man's quest for better living standards. Huge strides were made locally, particularly in the technical development of mass transport and long-distance communication. There were also other major advances in the discovery and development of chemicals and new materials like plastic. Once these discoveries were introduced into the manufacturing process they would bring about a revolution that would change just about every aspect of the way we live.

The achievements of the early visionaries, who constantly struggled to solve difficult problems, often before the appropriate technology became available, must be viewed from today's perspective as a truly remarkable feat of perseverance. In many instances the dedication and ingenuity shown by these early entrepreneurs and experimenters have added much to our knowledge and shaped the way that we think, live, work and play. Their endeavours and personal sacrifices should never be forgotten.

BRITAIN'S FIRST COMMERCIAL PORCELAIN FACTORY

Earlier we saw how the Cistercian monks brought prosperity and a diversity of industry to Stratford and in this section we shall discover how an individual from across the Irish Sea brought art, craftsmanship and beauty to what would become a rather grimy and polluted area.

Porcelain, a ceramic material made from white china clay and feldspar and fired in a kiln at temperatures of between 1,250 and 1,300 degrees centigrade, was first conceived by the Chinese in about the seventh or eighth century AD. The formula for the material, which had developed over time, remained a secret to the Western world for hundreds of years. The first shipments of porcelain began to arrive in Britain and the West by the early fourteenth century and the wares were mostly of the bluish glazed and lustrous white types.

A selection of Bow Porcelain on display at the Victoria & Albert Museum, Kensington, London.

Porcelain's arrival in the marketplace must have presented those early consumers with a range of new products that had an immediate aesthetic appeal in relation to what had been traditionally on offer. It would probably be fair to describe the tablewares that were then in common use as quite rudimentary objects that were functional and not necessarily designed to be pleasing to look at. Now, having articles available that were visually more attractive would have made them a popular choice with the buying public. Linked to porcelain's desirable features was the fact that these new products could be sold at low prices, making them a marketing success. These wares can be looked upon as the 'must have' articles of their day with an appeal to tempt a wide range of people. This no doubt provoked consumer demand, which in turn encouraged the Chinese manufacturers to increase their production capacity. These were the most likely causes that led the Chinese to ship porcelain in vast quantities to the markets of the West.

With such a product success story, it seems remarkable that it was not until the eighteenth century, almost four hundred years after the first shipments arrived in the West, that people in Britain began the process of trying to copy the Chinese manufacturers in the production of porcelain. Observing the written accounts and examining the scholarly research on the beginning of porcelain manufacture in Britain, it would appear that the establishment of a factory in east London came about by a combination of chance meetings or perhaps random introductions of men from different commercial and artistic backgrounds.

Thomas Frye was only twenty-two when he left Dublin, his place of birth, for England in 1732. Little is known of Frye's early life but he must have received some form of artistic training as in 1738 he was commissioned by the Saddlers' Company of London to paint a full-length portrait of H.R.H. Frederick, Prince of Wales. Only six years after this commission, on the 6 December 1744, patent number 610 was granted to "Edward Heylyn, in the Parish of Bow, in the County of Middlesex, Merchant, and Thomas Frye, of the Parish of Westham, in the County of Essex, Painter." The patent refers to "at last invented and brought to perfection A New Method of Manufacturing a Certain Material, whereby a Ware might be made of the same Nature or Kind, and equal to, if not exceeding in goodness and beauty, China or Porcelain Ware imported from Abroad...". This would appear to be one of the earliest references to the serious manufacture of porcelain in Britain.

As suggested earlier, the coming together of Edward Heylyn and Thomas Frye was possibly one of those chance meetings. The Saddlers' Company, of which Helwyn was a Freeman, had

Thomas Frye (1710–62) who came from Ireland and founded the Bow Porcelain Factory.

probably caused the two men to meet, perhaps when Frye was offered the painting commission. Interestingly, the wording of the patent, "at last invented and brought to perfection", provides us with a clue that the development of the formula to manufacture porcelain had not been particularly straightforward and had probably taken some years to reach a successful conclusion. It might also be possible to speculate that as Heylyn was described in the patent as a merchant (research has shown that he was a clothier) and Frye was known to be a painter and engraver, that it was Frye, rather than Heylyn who was responsible for persevering with the formulation of English porcelain. While it is not possible to be absolutely sure which of the two men first came up with the formula, or for that matter the idea to manufacture porcelain in Britain, there are some further clues that we should consider.

At the time, going through the processes of applying for a patent could easily take a year before authority was finally granted; and, taking into account the development of the processes to make porcelain, it is probable that there would have been several years of experiment preceding the patent. (In the eighteenth century, much of this work was a matter of trial and error as the science of materials and furnace firing temperatures had yet to be fully understood.) Given this background, it is probably fair to ask which

A.D. 1749 . . . . . . Nº 649.

Manufacture of Earthenware.

FRYE'S SPECIFICATION.

TO ALL TO WHOM THESE PRESENTS SHALL COME, I, THOMAS FRYE, of the Parish of West Ham, in the County of Essex, Painter, send greeting.

WHEREAS His most Excellent Majesty King George the Second, by His Letters Patent under the Great Seal of Great Britain, bearing date the Seventeenth day of November, in the twenty-third year of His reign, did give and grant unto me, the said Thomas Frye, His especial licence that I, the said Thomas Frye, during the term of years therein expressed, should and lawfully might make, use, exercise, and vend my "NEW METHOD OF MAKING A CERTAIN WARE, WHICH IS NOT INFERIOR IN BEAUTY AND FINENESS, AND IS RATHER SUPERIOR IN STRENGTH, THAN THE EARTHENWARE THAT IS BROUGHT FROM THE EAST INDIES, AND IS COMONLY KNOWN BY THE NAME OF CHINA, JAPAN, OR PORCELAIN WARE;" in which said Letters Patent there is contained a proviso obliging me, the said Thomas Frye, by a writing under my hand and seal, to cause a particular description of the nature of the said Invention, and in what manner the same is to be performed, to be inrolled in His Majesty's High Court of Chancery within four kalendar months after the date of the said recited Letters Patent, as in and by the same (relation being thereunto had) may more at large appear.

NOW KNOW YE, that in complyance with the said provisoe, I, the said Thomas Frye, do hereby declare that the said Invention is to be [performed in the manner following (that is to say) :—

As there is nothing in nature but by calcination, grinding, and washing will produce a fixed indissoluble matter, distinguished by the name of virgin earth, the properties of which is strictly the same whether produced from

Thomas Frye's 1749 specification for the "Manufacture of Earthenware".

of the two men would have been the most likely to have developed the process? Perhaps there is a further clue in patent number 649, registered solely in Frye's name on 17 November 1749. Here Frye refers to "my New Method of Making a Certain Ware, which is not Inferior in Beauty and Fineness, and is rather Superior in Strength, than the Earthenware that is brought from the East Indies, and is commonly known by the name of China, Japan, or Porcelain Ware."

After weighing up all the above evidence, on balance it would probably be fair to conclude that Frye was the most likely of the two men to have developed the process to produce English porcelain. However, when analysing historical evidence, things are not always straightforward as interpretations made and conclusions drawn over two hundred and fifty years later can often be flawed. Having said that, it is also fair to say that our understanding of a subject can often be enhanced by making an assumption, or drawing a conclusion, as from here debate can follow.

From the researches of Hugh Tait and others, who are authorities on early English porcelain, it has been established that, around 1744, Edward Heylyn and an Alderman George Arnold jointly purchased land and buildings on the west side of the River Lea, in the Parish of Bow. Here, on this site, it is believed that Frye's early experiments with porcelain had begun. Interestingly, Arnold was a Master of the Haberdashers' Company and his profession was that of a linen draper. Here again we see one of those seemingly chance connections, between the clothier Heylyn and the linen draper Arnold, alluded to earlier.

By at least March 1749 it is known that Arnold had established the Bow China Works on the east side of the River Lea in the Stratford Ward of the parish of West Ham and was operating under the name of "Alderman Arnold & Company". This he did until March 1750 when the name appears to have changed to "Messrs. Porcelain Company". The location of the factory was between Cook's Road

An engraving of Bow Bridge, c.1800, looking southwest. The artist appears to have been positioned near the confluence of the Bow Back River and the River Lea. This was quite close to the site of the Bow China Works.

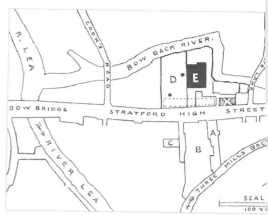

A map drawn by Aubrey J. Toppin, c.1922. The various letters refer as follows to:
X: Probable site of main factory building
E: Toppins' finds in 1922
D: Finds in 1921
A, B & C: Messrs. Bell & Black's match factory, finds in 1867

A late-eighteenth-century watercolour by Jefferyes Hammett O'Neale. Below the picture is written "taken from behind ye China House at Bow".

An unusual pair of lock gates on the Bow Back River close to the site of Thomas Frye's Bow Porcelain Factory. Note how the gates have been configured to hold back tides that can come from either direction.

and Marshgate Lane, on the north side of Stratford High Street. A modern multi-storey housing development now occupies the east end of the site.

By 25 September 1750 the name of the firm had again changed to "Fry and Company". Arnold died in June 1751 at the age of sixty. It is probably fair to conclude that he had been the major backer of Frye's porcelain experiments and had also provided the financial support to manufacture the products for the mass markets.

In the Heylyn and Frye patent of 1744, a material, named by the Cherokee Indians as 'Unaker' (a china clay or kaolin), was to be obtained from America. It would seem that the high quality of this material, coupled with its low cost, was mainly responsible for Frye being able to sell his wares at very competitive prices. When Frye took out his patent, in his own name alone in 1749, 'Unaker' is not mentioned, but pipe clay now appears in the text. It can also be deduced from the patent's wording that Frye had added a further ingredient, phosphate of lime (obtained by calcinating animal bones) to his formula. This produced a stronger material less prone to damage from rough handling. Today the material is more familiarly known as bone china.

Scholars and researchers have debated the 'Unaker' aspect of the patent and have not all agreed as to how long it was used, by Frye, in the manufacture of porcelain, if at all. Hugh Tait, on the other hand, has come up with some convincing evidence to suggest that Frye continued to use the material and, on balance, his arguments seem sound.

The Stratford factory was known as 'New Canton' and it has been suggested that it acquired this name because the works had been modelled along the lines of the most efficient of the Chinese factories in that district. In its heyday, in the late 1750s, while under Frye's control, the factory employed some three hundred workers, ninety of whom were skilled porcelain painters; many had come from Staffordshire, then centre of the British pottery industry.

The success of Bow porcelain was not just about producing a range of desirable low-cost wares for everyday home consumption: the factory also manufactured a range of exquisitely crafted and highly decorative figures, cutlery handles, plates, bowls, jugs, vases and other attractive ornaments. Added to this, there was a marketing and promotional element provided by a sales agent, Messrs. Weatherby & Crowther. This firm had a warehouse at St Catherine, near the Tower of London, and a retail outlet in Cornhill. It would appear that Weatherby & Crowther had strong business links with Frye and the Bow China Works. Hugh Tait has suggested that "the Bow China Works' wholesale and retail business, at least, was taken over and run by Weatherby & Crowther at some time after 1752". It is known that Bow wares were arriving in the markets of North America by the early 1750s. Therefore, it is possible, as some scholars have suggested that Weatherby & Crowther were well known throughout the world, that it was this firm who were responsible for the export of Bow wares.

By 1759 Frye's health had begun to deteriorate. Working and experimenting for many years in less-than-ideal conditions close to hot furnaces had probably accounted for this. Therefore, Frye took the decision to retire to Wales. However, sometime later he returned to London to once again take up portrait painting, specialising in miniatures. Frye died in 1762, in his fifty-second year, and was buried in Hornsey churchyard, north London.

The administrative arrangements for running the Bow China Works after Frye's death are not entirely clear, but we do know that, in 1776, the business was sold to William Duesbury, a potter from the midlands. All production, along with models and moulds, was transferred to Duesbury's works in Derby. This brought to an end one of the most aesthetically pleasing and artistically creative periods in West Ham's history; all started by a young portrait painter, Thomas Frye, from across the Irish Sea.

Note
There have been two archaeological excavations of the Bow China Factory site: one in 1922 led by Aubrey J. Toppin; and the other in 1969, when a further investigation was carried out under the direction of Dr David Redstone. In Anton Gabszewicz's brilliantly illustrated book, *Made in New Canton*, there are pictures of some of the 1969 finds.

WALTER HANCOCK
Another significant milestone in Newham's industrial development came about when Walter Hancock, an early transport engineer set up his business in Stratford around 1824, on the south side of Stratford High Street. Born at Marlborough, Wiltshire, he was the sixth son of James Hancock, a timber merchant and cabinet maker. Walter had initially served an apprenticeship to a London watchmaker and jeweller and it seems strange that someone trained in dealing with delicate jewellery and intricate mechanisms would eventually become one of the most innovative and successful steam engineers of the day, involved with the design and development of heavy mechanical road transport.

Walter Hancock (1799–1852) one of the earliest pioneers in the development of mass road transport.

From the late eighteenth century, men like Richard Trevithick and a few others had experimented with different types of steam transport but it was not until the 1820s that engineers began in earnest to tackle the many practical problems of moving people by road. It would therefore seem reasonable to speculate that the interest of this later group had been stimulated by the experiments of those other engineers, like George Stephenson, who were developing the means to move people and goods by rail.

Hancock had wisely concluded that vehicles travelling over the somewhat questionable road surfaces of the period would present him with a greater number of engineering problems to overcome than had been encountered by those engineers who were developing steam engines to run on smooth rails. Early on he had realised that it was crucial for road vehicles to be made as lightweight as possible to reduce the risks of mechanical damage and also of becoming bogged down in the potholes that were an uncomfortable obstacle to the travelling public of the day. He had also wanted to ensure that any future public transport system based on road vehicles was safe, economical and reliable. Hancock, perhaps more than any other of his inventor peers, had appreciated that the safe transportation of passengers was fundamental to any design consideration so that public confidence in such a revolutionary method of travel could be quickly gained. Probably his biggest engineering task was to ensure that steam, contained under high pressure in close proximately to passengers, would not, in extreme circumstances, prove hazardous to a travelling public.

In the past, steam engine designers had developed thick-walled metal pressure vessels to contain the steam and to work a piston and cylinder system connected to a crank. This type of arrangement was both heavy and bulky and, if the pressure vessel exploded, as occasionally it was apt to do, the flying pieces of metal could prove fatal to anyone nearby. Hancock overcame the majority of these problems by designing a lightweight coke-fired engine that did not have a piston or cylinder. He also solved the explosive properties of the pressure vessel by designing a unique system that was devoid of metal. In Hancock's words "it has two flexible steam receivers, which are composed of several layers of canvas, firmly united together by coatings of dissolved caoutchouch or India rubber, and are thus enabled to resist a pressure of steam of sixty pounds upon the square inch". The arrangement can be likened to a pair of bellows that inflate and deflate alternatively, having a similar action to a cylinder and piston. Interestingly, India rubber and like materials would turn out to play an important part in Hancock's future career.

NARRATIVE

OF

TWELVE YEARS' EXPERIMENTS.

(1824—1836,)

DEMONSTRATIVE

OF

THE PRACTICABILITY AND ADVANTAGE

OF EMPLOYING

STEAM-CARRIAGES

ON

COMMON ROADS:

WITH

Engravings and Descriptions

OF

THE DIFFERENT STEAM-CARRIAGES CONSTRUCTED BY THE AUTHOR.
HIS PATENT BOILER, WEDGE-WHEELS, AND OTHER INVENTIONS.

[STEAM PHAETON.]

BY WALTER HANCOCK, ENGINEER.

Hancock's *Narrative of Twelve Years' Experiments (1824–1836) Demonstrative of the Practicability and Advantage of Employing Steam Carriages on Common Roads*. These experiments were carried out at the Stratford works and on various roads in the locality.

The *Enterprise*, constructed at Stratford in 1833, was capable of carrying fourteen people. This was one of several innovative steam carriages built locally by Hancock.

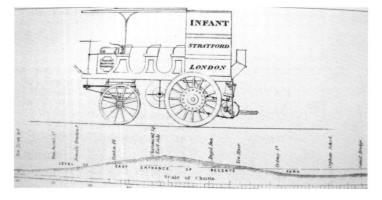

A line drawing of Hancock's *Infant* shown against the gradient of Pentonville Hill.

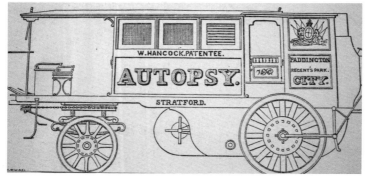

A drawing of Walter Hancock's steam road coach 'Autopsy' built at Stratford in east London in 1833.

A drawing of Walter Hancock's steam road coach 'ERA' built at Stratford in east London in 1834.

A picture of Walter Hancock's steam road coach 'ERA' built at Stratford in east London in 1834.

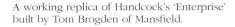

Tom Brogden in the cab of 'Enterprise' outside the Pump House Transport Museum in South Access Road, Walthamstow during the AEC centenary celebrations of 2010.

A working replica of Handcock's 'Enterprise' built by Tom Brogden of Mansfield.

Over a period of about fifteen years, Hancock produced a number of novel steam-carriage designs which he tested and modified, using the practical experience he had gained by driving them around the streets of London and further afield, under all manner of conditions. He appears to have given up on his India-rubber-coated pressure vessel quite early in his experimental programme, perhaps because the material became unreliable as improved vehicle designs called for increased steam pressures. However, Hancock never gave up on the notion of passenger safety and greater efficiency. By the late 1820s he had abandoned his experiments of trying to improve the working of conventional water-tube boilers (those which relied on hot gasses from the fire-box rising and heating the water in a system of pipes) for his own invention, the safer and more efficient 'chamber boiler'. This he patented in 1827 and it became recognised as one of the most powerful and safest of light boilers to be used in steam carriages.

THE GREAT EASTERN RAILWAY WORKS

At about the time when Hancock was considering abandoning his work on manufacturing steam carriages for use on roads, the establishment of the locomotive and carriage works of the Great Eastern Railway at Stratford began. This has allowed generations of trainspotters, those for whom there is something wondrous and beautiful about an engine that can run on rails belching smoke and steam while pulling a line of carriages or wagons, to indulge their hobby for over a century.

In 1848, the Eastern Counties Railway, as it was then known, moved its main locomotive workshops from Romford in Essex to a site in London's East End – located north east of Stratford High Street. It would appear that the Northern & Eastern Railway had already established a small repair shop at Stratford by 1839 and it was this facility which the Eastern Counties Railway leased in January 1844, perhaps with a view to the move in 1847–8. However, at the time, it is doubtful if the consolidation of the maintenance facility would be seen by those early planners as starting a process which was to alter radically the social and economic face of Stratford for over a hundred years. From a site of about fifteen acres and a workforce of a few hundred around the middle of the nineteenth century, the facility had grown to seventy-eight acres and employed over six thousand by the early part of the twentieth century. By the 1920s, the area occupied by the Great Eastern Railway, as it had become known in 1863, had almost doubled to approximately one hundred and thirty-three acres. This included the adjacent wagon-building and repair facility at Temple Mills.

A view of the general offices of the Great Eastern Railway Works, Stratford, East London, c.1920, after alterations had taken place. Note the design of the weather vane.

The move to Stratford not only brought the construction of new buildings, which would eventually lead to the carrying out of just about every type of rolling-stock repair imaginable, but also the building of three hundred homes to house the workforce and their families. Soon the district became known locally as "Hudson's Town" after the railway entrepreneur, George Hudson. As late as the 1950s, the area was referred to as the "New Town" by residents with long memories or those with railway connections. Even today, names like Waddington Road and Waddington Street (after Hudson's traffic manager) remind us of the area's railway heritage.

The Drawing Office of the Great Eastern Railway Works, Stratford, East London, c.1920.

An engine under construction at the Great Eastern Railway Works, Stratford, East London.

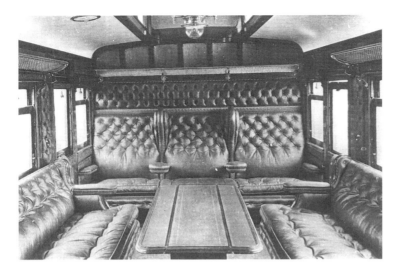

A first-class railway carriage after being upholstered at the Great Eastern Railway Works, Stratford, East London.

The Claud Hamilton, one of several express (4-4-0) engines built at the Great Eastern Railway Works, Stratford, East London.

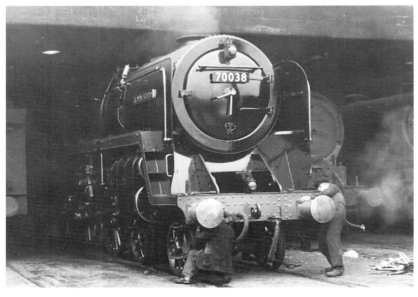

The Robin Hood (4-6-0) being prepared at Stratford for an exhibition at Southend, Essex in 1956. After Nationalisation in 1948, the works lost its Great Eastern Railway title and became British Railways.

The coat of arms of the Great Eastern Railway.

James Holden, superintendent of the Great Eastern Railway Works, standing in front of the 'Decapod' (0-10-0) railway engine, c.1902. Although Holden was responsible for the engineering development of this engine, much of the design was completed by the talented railway engineer Fred Russell.

Over the years, the railway works at Stratford were home to several notable engineers and superintendents, who were responsible for the introduction of many new ideas and much technical innovation. In 1850, under John Viret Gooch, the works completed their first railway engine. This suggests a major change of direction for the company, as it would have required a considerable amount of capital investment to complete such a venture. At the time, it must have been obvious to those responsible that once tooling-up for engine building had begun, there would be a need for ongoing investment in plant and machinery as the future technology of railway engines and other rolling stock changed. Also, it will be remembered that the Stratford works was heavily committed to providing a maintenance and repair service for the Great Eastern Railway which, in the years to come, would no doubt become more complex as the amount of rolling stock in circulation increased. However, it would appear that the decision to build railway engines was successful, as construction lasted at Stratford up until the 1920s. During this period, 1,682 locomotives were built along with some 5,500 passenger vehicles and in excess of 33,000 goods wagons. This would equate to a complete engine being turned out every two weeks over a period of seventy years – a remarkable achievement.

Other remarkable achievements occurred, particularly when Stratford was under the superintendence of James Holden, when the works responded to a number of engineering challenges. In February 1888 the Crewe works of the London North Western Railway had built a locomotive in 25.5 hours. This record was

The 'Decapod' under construction at the Great Eastern Railway Works.

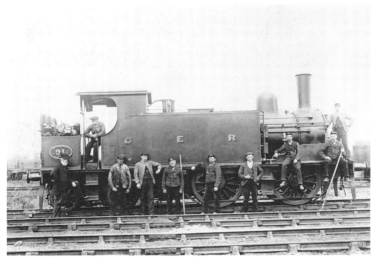

James Holden, in bowler hat, superintendent of the Great Eastern Railway Works, standing with crew and railway workers in front of a 0-4-4 engine, c.1897.

A photograph of the eighty-five workmen who were responsible for building Engine No. 930 (0-6-0) in world record time. The engine was also given a coat of grey paint before it began trials.

quickly eclipsed in America by June the same year, at the Altoona works of the Pennsylvania Railway, when the time was lowered to 16.5 hours. The challenge was taken up by the Stratford works when, in December 1891, the time for construction was brought down to 9 hours and 47 minutes – a world record for this class of engine. This record was never beaten.

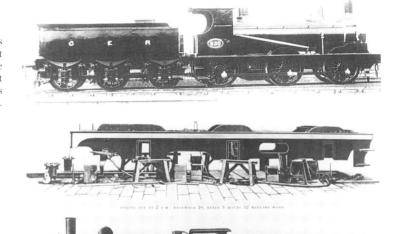

Engine No. 930 (0-6-0) was given an undercoat when it was built but did not receive its top coat of paint until it had completed 36,000 miles hauling coal.

Engine No. 930 (0-6-0), built in the world record time of 9 hours and 47 minutes over two days, 10–11 December 1891, at the Great Eastern Railway Works, Stratford, East London.

THE THAMES IRONWORKS

It is probably fair to argue that steam did more to advance the technological development of Newham than any other power source. The evidence for this can be seen not only in the stories of Hancock and the Great Eastern Railway works, but also the shipyard of Ditchburn and Mare that was situated on the Middlesex bank of the River Lea, close to where the waterway enters the River Thames, an area commonly known as Leamouth. On maps, this section of the river is referred to as Bow Creek.

By the mid-1840s, the yard was finding it difficult to obtain supplies of iron at competitive rates. Bringing in the material by rail would have been expensive, as the main line ran through Stratford, some distance from the yard. If Stratford had been used, it would have meant transferring iron to horse-drawn wagons for the final part of

An engraving showing part of the inside of the C.J. Mare & Company shipbuilding works at Blackwall, east London, c.1854. Note the giant Nasmyth steam hammer (named after the famous Victorian engineer, James Nasmyth) towards the centre of the picture. Mare's works had seven of these heavy stamping tools.

An engraving showing a general view of the C.J. Mare & Company shipbuilding works at Blackwall in east London, c.1854. On the left bank of the waterway is the Essex yard and on the right bank the Middlesex yard. The waterway is the River Lea just before it enters the River Thames. This section of the Lea is known as Bow Creek.

Bow Creek looking south towards the River Thames as it appeared in 1998.

An early picture of the Thames Ironworks main building and yard at Canning Town.

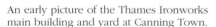

Workmen posing for the picture in the Thames Ironworks foundry.

Launching into Bow Creek from the eastern slipway in the late nineteenth century.

A section of the first Blackwall Tunnel that was fabricated at the Thames Ironworks.

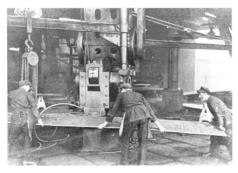

Cutting iron plate at the Thames Ironworks.

A memorial to Charles J. Mare, the founder of the engineering firm that became the Thames Ironworks.

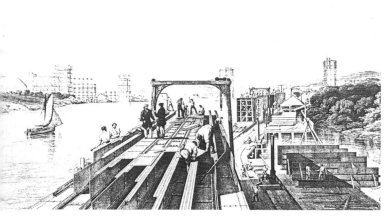

the journey. At the time, the North Woolwich branch of the Eastern Counties and Thames Junction railway had not yet been completed.

To resolve the yard's difficulties, Mare suggested to his partner that they should set up their own facility to roll iron plate. Clearly Ditchburn was not sympathetic to the idea and the partnership dissolved. In 1846, the new firm of C.J. Mare & Co. was established on the opposite side of the River Lea in Essex. The move was to mark not only a significant milestone in the history of British shipbuilding, but that of the world.

The coming of the Crimean War in 1853 saw an increase in both wood and iron shipbuilding. Mare's yard not only received orders from the British Admiralty but also from the French government. It is recorded that the yard built four wooden despatch vessels, four gunboats, two large despatch boats and some twelve iron mortar boats. Two floating batteries were also constructed for the French government, comprising a wooden shell plated with 3.5 inch (9cm) of armour. These were to be used for attacking the fortified coastal positions at the Crimea.

By 1856, Mare was in financial difficulty and the running of the company was taken over by his father-in-law, Peter Rolt, who assumed control as Chairman. The company name was changed to the Thames Ironworks & Shipbuilding Co. Soon, the new company was bidding for a British Admiralty contract to construct what was to become the largest warship afloat, the first sea-going ironclad in the world. *HMS Warrior*, powered by both sail and steam, was launched in December 1860 and was accepted into service by the Royal Navy. Despite being clad with 4 inch (10cm) of iron plate and weighing 9,210 tons, *Warrior* could achieve 17.5 knots with both power sources engaged.

Left: The Britannia Bridge over the Menai Straits under construction in c.1849 with box girders supplied by C.J. Mare & Company.

Above: I.K. Brunel's Royal Albert Bridge which took the railway over the River Tamar to Saltash in Cornwall. Built in 1859 with girders supplied by the Thames Ironworks and still in operation today (2010).

HMS Warrior, launched 29 December 1860. At the time, she was the largest sea-going iron-clad warship in the world.

The author standing in front of the restored *HMS Warrior* at her current berth in Portsmouth dockyard, July 1998.

HMS Warrior's restored Wardroom where the officers would dine. In time of battle the dining table would become the operating table.

A bank of four restored washing machines in the laundry area on board *HMS Warrior*. Note the handle, currently reversed to prevent accidents, which was used to revolve the clothes in the tubs. Also note that each machine has its own mangle to squeeze water from the clothes after washing.

View, looking along part of the upper deck towards the stern, of the restored *HMS Warrior*.

A breech-loading Armstrong 110-pounder gun mounted to the fore of the restored *HMS Warrior*. Note the brass slide and pivot tracks fastened to the deck which were used for positioning the gun.

A cut-away section of a cannon port showing iron plate bolted to teak.

Anchor chains on *HMS Warrior*.

It is difficult today to imagine that large-scale manufacturing industries such as ironworks and shipbuilding were operating at the southern end of the River Lea. Normally such industries are associated with Scotland, Northern Ireland and the north-east of England. Between the years 1840 and 1911 the Thames Ironworks, including sixteen years of C.J. Mare, was responsible for the construction of 278 merchant ships.

Perhaps even more remarkably, the Thames Ironworks, including ten years of C.J. Mare, built 144 warships. The last to be built at the yard was the 22,500 ton battleship *Thunderer*, which saw service with the Royal Navy during the First World War at the Battle of Jutland.

The *SS Yavari* built for the Peruvian Navy in 1862 at the Thames Ironworks, Canning Town, East London. She was shipped to Peru in pieces and carried up the Andes Mountains by mule train. Now she resides as a floating museum on Lake Titicaca 12,500 feet (3,810 m) above sea level, the highest Navigable waterway in the world.

Charles J. Mare

The Dreadnaught Class battleship *HMS Thunderer*, launched on 1 February 1911, the last major warship built at the Thames Ironworks.

Far left: The Thames Ironworks football team, late nineteenth century, the forerunner of West Ham United Football Club.

Left: Arnold Hills (1857–1927) the director of the Thames Ironworks who was responsible for establishing the works football team and a number of other sporting and social activities for the workforce.

The Thames Ironworks, in its heyday, ran six departments. These were: marine engines and motor cars, boatbuilding, cranes, electrical engineering, civil engineering and shipbuilding. During the company's remarkable history it was also involved in producing ironwork for a number of diverse civil engineering projects. Interestingly, the crossed hammers emblem on the shirts of West Ham United Football Club is a constant reminder of the club's founding origins. The hammers are in fact riveting hammers that were used extensively in the ship building industry.

SIR JOSEPH BAZALGETTE

By the mid nineteenth century, with Newham's industrial revolution gaining pace, an influx of artisans to support the growing industries was adding rapidly to the local population. The borough's out-dated sanitary arrangements were unable to cope. In recent years there had been a number of serious cholera outbreaks in London but the epidemics of 1849 and 1854 alone had claimed the lives of almost forty thousand people. While poor sanitation and lack of clean supplies of drinking water were thought to be the main causes of the problem, there were other contributory factors like the random dumping of household waste in the streets, which, over the years, had gone unchecked.

When the Romans built Londinium, their settlement by the Thames, in about AD 50, the river and its tributaries would have been clear and unpolluted. Since that time a gradual increase and then a rapid expansion in the population and their dwellings had taken place, putting considerable pressure on nature's resources, land and water. For example, in the first fifty years of the nineteenth century, the number of people living in the Capital had quadrupled. The Metropolis Management Act of 1855 defined London as having a population of almost 4,000,000 inhabitants living in 500,000 houses, which covered an area of 117 square miles. Apart from the increased levels of pollution created by such a large population, with their human waste leaching into rivers and streams, there was also the added problem of industrial effluent discharge as a growing number of factories were setting up in London. Over the years little had been done to deal with these mounting difficulties and the simple fact that the ground had been covered with buildings and roads meant that there was hardly any natural space to soak up surface rainwater. During wet weather, rain would mix with the untreated sewage from cesspools and other areas, causing extra run off into the already-polluted rivers and streams, which in turn could cause flooding. The results of having this noxious soup swilling around streets and houses can't have been pleasant for the inhabitants.

The term 'sewer' has not always meant a brick-lined tunnel built to take away household effluent. Various rivers and streams that took away surface water were often referred to as sewers; and until 1815 it was illegal to discharge sewage into conduits designated as water channels. Cesspools were the only places where household effluent could effectively be stored. Removing sewage from these receptacles was the job of the 'night men' who were not always particular as to where the unhygienic contents were dumped.

In 1848, the Metropolitan Commission of Sewers was set up to replace the eight district bodies that had been responsible for London's drainage. It is probably fair to suggest that as there had not been an overarching body to deal with drainage across the Capital, the sewer system, such as it was, had become something of a nightmare of ill-designed waterways, channels and tunnels. At district boundaries, sewers of different falls, shapes and sizes came together causing effluent back up (surcharge) and blockage. The inadequate system of disposing of effluent had not been helped by the introduction of the water closet into some of London's more affluent homes in the late eighteenth century. This had increased loading on the sewerage system as the flushing toilet became more popular. The situation had been considerably exacerbated when, in 1847, an Act was passed making it compulsory to drain the contents of cesspools into London's sewers. While this removed around 30,000 cesspools from the Capital in just a few years, it did mean that high levels of raw sewage were now entering the Thames, sometimes close to where water companies were extracting drinking water. The pollution of the river became so bad that, in 1855, an Act was passed "to prevent all sewage from the Metropolis flowing into the Thames". Of course, politicians sitting comfortably in parliament and passing an Act is one thing; making such a scheme happen is another.

In 1849, Joseph Bazalgette had been appointed a member of the Metropolitan Commission of Sewers. In the years following, several plans were submitted to the Commission for improving London's sewer system but none were implemented. However, in 1854 Bazalgette was directed to "prepare a scheme of intercepting sewers, intended to effect the improved Main Drainage of London, and Mr Haywood was associated with him for the northern portion". In February that year the famous civil engineer Sir William Cubitt reported that "after a very careful examination of the reports and plans, and the elaborate set of sections and details which they (Messrs, Bazalgette and Haywood) have produced, together with the estimate founded thereon, that the whole are worthy of every attention as regards the capacities and inclinations of the various intercepting drains, in relation to the quantities of water they have to carry and discharge." Although Cubitt had recommended that Bazalgette's and Haywood's plan be adopted the Commission still took no action.

The Victorian civil engineer Sir Joseph Bazalgette who was responsible for designing and planning London's sewerage system which is still in use today.

By 1856, the Metropolitan Board of Works had superseded the Metropolitan Commission of Sewers and Bazalgette assumed the role of Chief Engineer. Again Bazalgette was instructed to prepare a plan for the drainage of London and, when completed, it was approved and adopted by the Board. However, that was not the end of the matter. Her Majesty's First Commissioner of Works had the power of veto and once again the plan was blocked. It was not until 1859, after much frustration and negotiation that work finally began on Bazalgette's scheme. Interestingly, the previous year, there had been an extremely hot summer and the incoming tide in the Thames had caused large amounts of floating effluent to gather outside the Houses of Parliament. It was reported that the smell was so disgusting that curtains soaked in chloride of lime had to be hung over windows and doors in an effort to reduce the smell. The episode was known as the 'Great Stink' and it was probably this "effluent lobby of parliament" that created the necessary political will, which gave Bazalgette the final authority to begin work on his scheme.

An engraving showing cut-and-cover work for the high-level sewer as it crosses Victoria Park, Hackney, c.1860.

An engraving depicting workmen building an above-ground section of Bazalgette's sewer, c.1860s. This looks distinctly like the raised portion that takes the effluent from Stratford to Becton, which is called the Northern Outfall Sewer.

How many people, when taking their afternoon stroll along the Greenway, appreciate that they are walking along the top of Bazalgette's Northern Outfall Sewer built almost a century and a half ago?

An engraving of the Northern Outfall Sewer crossing the Channelsea River.

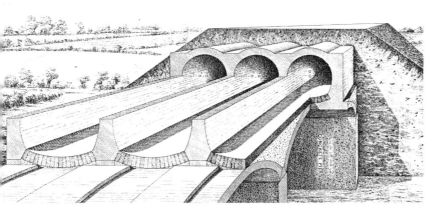

Cut-away drawing of a section of the above-ground Northern Outfall Sewer showing culverts and substructure.

A section of what appears to be the Northern Outfall Sewer which has yet to be completed. Towards the middle of the scene are three smartly clad gentlemen in top hats!

Bazalgette's grand plan was to have three intercepting sewers (high, middle and low level) north of the River Thames running west to east, all relying on gravity and using surface water to maintain the flow. On the south side of the river the three intercepting lines (high and low level plus the Effra Branch) all met at Deptford Creek. Here pumps were installed to lift the sewage eighteen feet (5.3 metres) into the Southern Outfall Sewer. From here the material was taken by gravity to Crossness on the Erith Marshes where massive steam engines pumped the waste into storage tanks, later to be discharged into the Thames on the ebb tide. Bazalgette had calculated that for sewage not to be returned on the incoming tide it would need to be discharged some fourteen miles below London Bridge.

At West Ham, on the north side of the Thames, the Abbey Mills pumping station was built to lift the effluent around forty feet (12 meters) from the low-level sewer to feed the Northern Outfall Sewer. Once there, gravity would take the material onward to Barking Creek where it would be stored in tanks to await discharge on the ebb tide. Bazalgette's massive scheme of approximately 1,300 miles of brick-built sewers took almost sixteen years to complete and is still the backbone of the London sewerage system today, playing a vital part in the maintenance of the Capital's health in the twenty-first century. Fortunately, in recent years, there has been increased interest in the preservation of industrial buildings and Abbey Mills stand as a memorial to Victorian engineering ingenuity, in an area of Stratford that is fast regenerating.

A nineteenth-century engraving of the Abbey Mills Pumping Station. Apart from the twin towers being demolished in 1941, to make the site a less obvious target for German bombers, the building still retains many of its original features.

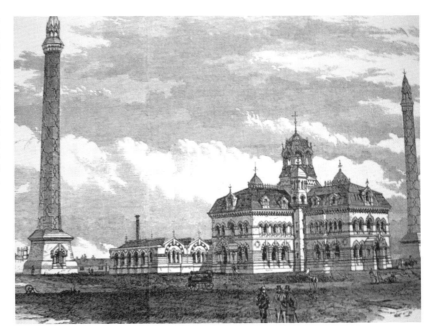

An engraving showing the inside of the Abbey Mills Pumping Station with its profusion of intricate Victorian ironwork. Although the pumping station is now only used in emergencies in cases of severe flooding, the ironwork remains in all its Victorian glory.

The Abbey Mills Pumping Station has been listed Grade II* by English Heritage and is a fine example of Victorian architecture.

Some of the beautifully proportioned mid-nineteenth-century houses that were built in Abbey Lane for the workers and their families at the Abbey Mills Pumping Station.

Abbey Mills storm-water outlets that discharge into the Channelsea River to prevent flooding during heavy rainfall.

The massive base of one of the twin chimneys, demolished in 1941, that still remains in the grounds of the pumping station.

The Abbey Mills pumping station was constructed on a really grand scale in the form of a crucifix with a central lantern, mansard roof and dormer windows. It included ornamental brickwork, arched windows, sculptured masonry, expensive wall tiles and, on the inside, a profusion of decorative and lavishly constructed ironwork. To finish off the construction, the architect, Charles Driver, designed two highly ornate Moorish-style chimneys, each one hundred and ninety feet (58 metres) tall.

These took away the exhaust from the boilers that fed eight beam engines located (a pair in each section) within the four sections of the cruciform shape. The building became known as the 'Cathedral of Sewage' and was sometimes referred to as 'a mosque in the marshes'. Sadly, in 1941, the chimneys were demolished after bombs damaged some of the site's low-level buildings. At the time it was thought that the chimneys provided the German aircrews with a highly visible landmark to target the London docks. However, the bases of the chimneys still remain.

The modern state-of-the-art pumping station, to a design developed by Thames Water engineers and commissioned in 1997. This facility is one of the largest sewage pumping stations in the world, serving over one million people in London and other low-lying areas north of the Thames.

While Bazalgette's sewers are still keeping the population of London healthy, the large over-ground Northern Outfall section that currently cuts a swathe through Newham's landscape has a brand new path built on top to allow the large crowds of visitors safe access to the 2012 Olympic Park. I am sure Sir Joseph would have been proud of such a memorial that not only connects his legacy to the health of London but also to the 2012 Olympic and Paralympic Games.

THE LONDON DOCKS AND GEORGE PARKER BIDDER

It would be an unforgivable omission by any author, when writing a chapter that relates to the history of Newham, not to mention George Parker Bidder's early involvement with the borough. Although not a local man, his civil-engineering projects and collaborations, begun locally in the 1840s, determined the pattern of industrial and commercial development that brought economic prosperity and employment to the area. Bidder's early work established a model that, although changed by the ravages of war and time, has acted as the template for the massive regeneration projects that we see around us in the borough and adjacent districts today. *The Victoria History of the County of Essex* states that "Bidder, more than any other person, was the maker of modern West Ham."

George Parker Bidder (1806–1879), "the maker of modern West Ham"

A drawing of George Parker Bidder, the calculating boy, as a young man.

George Parker Bidder was born of humble stock at Moreton Hampstead, a small village on the edge of Dartmoor, Devon on 14 June 1806 where his father was a stonemason. When of age, young George was sent to the village school but it would seem that he took every opportunity to play truant. Fortunately George's elder brother gave him rudimentary tuition in counting but the lessons only lasted until the lad had learned to reach one hundred. However, the lessons appear to have kindled an imaginative spark as George began to take more than a passing interest in the structure of numbers. To amuse himself he would arrange objects such as marbles or items of lead shot in lines and squares. From these games he soon learned, for example, that a square with eight objects on each of its sides would contain a total block of sixty-four objects. Before he knew the meaning of the word, he had taught himself the art of multiplication.

Once George had mastered these fundamentals, his powers of mental arithmetic rapidly grew. When he was about seven he overheard two people in his village arguing over the weight and price of a pig that one of them was selling. The story goes that he went up to the protagonists and said "you are both wrong"; then, to their amazement, proceeded to give them the correct price of the animal. Several years later, when delivering a paper to the Institution of Civil Engineers, George related the story of how, as a child, he had been befriended by the village blacksmith whom he described as "a kind old man, not having any children". Apparently the blacksmith's shop was the centre of village gossip and young George was allowed to amuse himself around the forge. Sometimes, as a treat, he would be allowed to work the bellows. Bidder explained to the meeting that while in the company of the blacksmith he, for some inexplicable reason, had given the correct answer to a calculation. This had so astonished the people around him that he had been asked to solve more difficult questions, all of which he apparently answered correctly. In the words of Bidder "this increased my fame still more, and what was better, it eventually caused halfpence to flow into my pocket; which I need not say, had the effect of attaching me still more to the science of arithmetic". It would seem that young George's fame was spreading and he was becoming a popular attraction. People were attaching such names to him as the "calculating phenomenon" and the "calculating boy".

George's father, no doubt perceiving that he had the makings of a fortune on his hands, took the boy around the country, where his talents were exploited for money. It was not long before the lad's fame had spread to the ruling classes and in 1815, when only nine years old, the Bishop of Salisbury introduced him to Her Majesty Queen Charlotte. On this occasion, he gave the titled audience a demonstration of solving intricate questions quickly and with great accuracy.

While travelling the country, George's general education suffered. It was therefore fortunate that young George's mathematical exploits had come to the notice of the Reverend Thomas Jephson, Fellow and Tutor of St. John's College, Cambridge. In 1817 Jephson, along with a colleague, Sir John Herschel, visited the lad's family at Moreton Hampstead and persuaded them to allow George to be properly educated, agreeing that he and friends at Cambridge would cover the cost. It would seem that George's mother readily agreed to the arrangement although his father was at first reluctant to give his blessing. Eventually, George was placed with a Reverend W. Jephson, the master of a Grammar School at Camberwell, London. There he stayed for about a year until his father removed him. Once more George was taken around the country to earn money for his father. Luckily, George's Cambridge sponsors were able to intervene and this time he was taken to Edinburgh to continue his education. While there he caught the attention of Sir Henry Jardine, a high-ranking official who, along with some titled friends, arranged for the lad to receive private tuition from a Reverend A. Stewart. Afterwards, in 1819, George attended classes at the University of Edinburgh and, in 1822, the magistrates of Edinburgh awarded him a prize for the study of higher mathematics.

A painting of a group of Victorian engineers, with George Parker Bidder standing behind his friend, the railway engineer Robert Stephenson, who is seated at the centre of the table.

While at university, George had become good friends with his sponsor Sir Henry Jardine and had also made the acquaintance of Robert Stephenson (son of the engineer George Stephenson, of 'Rocket' fame) who was later to become a railway and civil engineer of considerable standing. This latter relationship was to have a marked effect on George's later professional career. George left university in 1824 and Jardine used his influence to get him a job with the Ordnance Survey. This allowed George to get a foot on the professional ladder. Bidder never forgot the kindness that Jardine had shown him and some years later, as a mark of respect for his sponsor and also to thank his old university for his tutoring, he founded the Jardine Bursary with a grant of £40 per year to help poor students obtain a decent education.

In 1825, on the advice of friends, Bidder left the Ordnance Survey and began work at the office of the civil engineer, Henry Robinson Palmer, who in that year had raised his personal profile by building the world's first monorail across open country at Cheshunt, Hertfordshire. Palmer first employed Bidder in work on the eastern entrance of the London Docks. Afterwards, this was followed by several surveys of canals and railways. No doubt the experience gained from working on Palmer's civil-engineering contracts had given Bidder the confidence to look for new challenges. Only four years after joining Palmer, he took up a position with another firm of civil engineers, Walker & Burgess, where he was first involved with the laying of a granite tramway in London's Commercial Road. Over forty years later, when the tramway was removed, it was reported by the civil engineer J.B. Redman that "the original stones were still in place, due in a great measure to the excellent way in which the road was laid".

By the early 1830s, Bidder had been appointed assistant engineer on a construction project at the Brunswick wharf, Blackwall. Here he took the bold decision to introduce cast-iron piles and plates to the project. It is believed that this is the first occasion that such techniques of civil engineering had been employed in this way.

Bidder's real professional breakthrough came in 1834 when he was invited by his old acquaintance, Robert Stephenson, to take up a challenging appointment on the London and Birmingham railway, a project that was already engaging the country's best civil-engineering brains. In fact, it was the construction of this particular railway that was to connect the London Docks with Britain's industrial heartland that brought much commercial wealth to the east London locality. In the mid-1830s, Bidder became connected with George Stephenson in parliamentary work associated with railway and other projects. Here Bidder's powers of rapid calculation came to the fore when, over the years, he appeared before many parliamentary committees as an expert witness where he was in his element. Using his unique skills, Bidder was able to challenge the economic viability of projects put forward by other prominent engineers, even such famous names as Isambard Kingdom Brunel.

In his lifetime, Bidder was responsible and associated with a wide range of high-profile civil-engineering projects, not only in Britain, but also abroad. However, it is probably fair to conclude that of all

An aerial photograph of the Royal Docks taken in the 1960s. This image is reproduced from the *Victoria County History: Essex, Vol. 6,* by permission of the General Editor.

Above left: An aerial photograph of the Royal Docks today, now the site of London City Airport where aircraft designed for short take off and landing (STOL) operate.

Above right: Dockers unloading a cargo of meat, c.1960. The London Docks was a major employer of local people and did much to enhance Britain's growing economy.

his local projects, his greatest legacy to the borough of West Ham was his vision and determination to construct the Victoria Docks, officially opened in 1855 by Albert, Prince Consort and named in honour of the Queen. For its day, this was a vast undertaking covering almost one hundred acres of deep-water berthing, with extensive warehousing and quay space. The project was supported by a system of large locks with massive outward-curving iron lock gates – at the time a great innovation and also the largest operating in London. Their use was for maintaining water levels in the dock areas that would have otherwise been subjected to the tidal vagaries of the River Thames. Bidder employed hydraulic power to work the lock machinery and also to operate the cranes that were used for loading and unloading the ships. In building the dock walls, Bidder innovatively made great use of cast-iron piling and he also used considerable amounts of concrete in the construction. These techniques reduced the need for building a costly cofferdam; a method that, at the time, was usually employed by civil engineers in such construction projects.

When conceiving the idea for building the Victoria Docks on, what was then, the Essex marshes, Bidder had recommended that a larger area of land be purchased for future dock expansion. This remarkable piece of foresight, which at the time was considered by many to be a wholly foolhardy enterprise that was doomed to fail, was in later years to pay considerable dividends. When the docks were extended later in the century, it was reported that, in the interim period, land prices had spiralled upward by several hundred per cent.

It is clear that Bidder's vision for dock development had paved the way, in later years, for the building of the Royal Albert and King

George V Docks. These improved facilities for shipping created wealth and jobs as new industries and commerce were attracted to the area. This, in turn, helped to promote the expansion of the road and rail infrastructure (Bidder himself had acted as engineer during the construction of the Eastern Counties and Thames Junction Railway, popularly known as the North Woolwich Line).

While the maritime heritage of the region has declined dramatically, particularly during the second half of the twentieth century, there is now the modern London City Airport, with its runway situated close to the former Victoria and Albert Docks. Perhaps local people should use this prominent landmark as a memorial to the expertise and vision of George Parker Bidder, who, with his army of workmen, created modern West Ham.

THE CONTINUING JOURNEY

As the reader, you may be wondering why we have just travelled on a journey through history in what might appear to be a series of unconnected steps – from Cistercian Monks to Thomas Frye's Bow Porcelain factory, onward to Stratford's Great Eastern Railway Works then, via the Thames Ironworks, to Bazalgette's Abbey Mills Pumping Station, finally arriving at the London Docks. You may also be wondering why I have chosen to include stories that I have written about before in earlier books in the Lea Valley series. Well, in truth, I have a confession to make. As my publisher has decided to make this book the last in the current Lea Valley series, I wanted to take this opportunity to suggest how the discoveries, inventions and the entrepreneurs of the past have influenced and moulded the way we live today and also to suggest how their legacy will determine how people live their lives in the future.

If we stop and think for a minute, it will soon be realised that much of the knowledge that we have acquired has been learned and handed down from the generation that came before. If we take this observation to its logical conclusion we will also recognise that our collective knowledge stretches back as far as the hunter gatherers and beyond. The knowledge that we have each acquired and accumulated will be modified and up-dated by personal experience as we travel through life and this store of information will be shared and will influence others. Then, either through a process of osmosis or by deliberate transfer, the information will eventually pass to the next generation. The stories that I have chosen (I could have included many others) can be used to explain how change takes place and, in particular, how we each adapt and modify our thinking as we learn from others.

When the Cistercian order established their abbey at Stratford, the area was a sparsely populated piece of land on the edge of the Thames marshes. As we have seen, the order was divided into two distinct classes and up until the dissolution of the monasteries the monks would have had a considerable influence on the development of Stratford and the surrounding area. Within the order there were those who indulged in worship and other spiritual duties while others, who should be looked upon as artisans, did the everyday work, from tilling the land which kept the abbey fed to providing the craft skills that maintained the abbey buildings, with their complex infrastructure requiring everything from masonry work to blacksmithing. Over the years, the community that grew up outside the abbey would have gained from its presence, benefiting from the skills that had been developed by the lower order of monks which eventually would help to shape today's bustling Newham.

Even after the destruction of the abbey by King Henry VIII in the sixteenth century, the knowledge and skills acquired and absorbed into the growing local community would not have been lost. Therefore, it is not unreasonable to speculate that these acquired skills and knowledge would be modified and improved by a process of trial and error and the best practices selected and adopted. Those that did not work would be rejected and after a time forgotten. Then, like an endless Olympic relay, the knowledge baton would be carried forward and handed to the next generation, who were then entrusted to pass it to the next generation in the expectation that they, in turn, would carry it forward.

Thomas Frye's arrival in Stratford and his building of the Bow Porcelain Works in the eighteenth century not only brought a new industry to the area; it also acted as a catalyst that attracted skilled artisans from different parts of the country. And because the factory did business with other countries around the world and competed with the Chinese porcelain industry, it is not hard to imagine how, in the process of trading, different skills were learned, exported and imported. This process is often referred to as 'spin out' and 'spin in'. From this example it can be seen how the transfer and sharing of technology and knowledge tends to develop and continue.

With the arrival of steam locomotion through Walter Hancock and later the Great Eastern Railway Works, it will be appreciated that Stratford was becoming a centre of engineering excellence. The rapid expansion of industry, particularly the Great Eastern Railway Works, again attracted artisans to the area, bringing with them a range of new skills and techniques. As industry became more technologically advanced, further new skills and techniques were developed and acquired. These new skills added to and built upon the skill base that had come before.

Almost in parallel with the engineering developments at Stratford came the foundation, at Canning Town, of the shipbuilding firm of Ditchburn and Mare which later became the Thames Ironworks. At about this time, the shipyard had begun moving away from the building of traditional wooden ships to the construction of larger and heavier vessels made from iron. Therefore, it will be appreciated that the use of this new material meant the learning and development of yet more new skills and techniques. This new industry also encouraged the setting up of a collection of new supply-chain companies that would work with the Ironworks to provide a range of products like engines, boilers, chains, ropes and paint. These new industries required power to drive their manufacturing machinery, which was initially provided by coal. This would have to be brought to the area mainly by rail and sea. So it is not unreasonable to surmise that improved designs of railway wagons and cargo ships would have to be built by the new emerging industries to bring the material from the coalfields, situated in the midlands and the north of the country. With the increased local demand for energy to feed the hungry industries, civil-engineering projects were encouraged to improve the handling capacity of the docks and the railway infrastructure, and direct routes were created to the coal towns.

As Stratford's manufacturing base grew so did the population of artisans and their families, who were drawn to the area to support the increasing demand for skilled labour that was required to service the spread of diverse industries. These new immigrants put pressure on the housing stock, the supply of clean water and wholesome food, and in particular the overall health and hygiene of the community. These latter problems were partially solved by the building of Bazalgette's London sewerage system and the modernisation and expansion of the London Docks which helped to cope with the increase in demand for food and materials.

However, as will be imagined, each expansion of industry and commerce created further demands which naturally attracted more people to the area, particularly those from the countryside seeking work. With each phase of an industrial expansion, there is usually an increased level of technological complexity and this in turn dictates a time when sections of the workforce must reach higher levels of competency. Research has indicated that the levels of literacy and numeracy were generally poor among the early workforce, particularly those arriving from working on the land; which means that the expansion of industry and commerce had created another demand. Now the focus was on education and training as the new workforce had to assimilate a range of different skills to service the burgeoning industries. This put pressure on the educational institutions, forcing the expansion of schools, colleges and technical institutes and also encouraged industry to develop specialist training.

In travelling this path from the past to the present, we have been able to discover the mechanism which helped our ancestors create the society, industry and commerce that has formed the blueprint for our modern world and given us the life support systems that we enjoy today. They did this through a process of technology transfer and knowledge sharing and we are the current recipients of their legacy. The evidence for this is all around us in the way our homes are lit and heated, how we travel, the way we shop and the new

New buildings are beginning to dominate the Stratford skyline, August 2010. However, the former Yardley building, to the right foreground, with its iconic image of the Flower Sellers adorning the building, is a reminder of Stratford's recent past. Yardley's left Stratford in 1966.

A new pathway along the top of Bazalgette's Northern Outfall Sewer
that links Stratford to Hackney Wick across the Olympic Park site.

The 2012 Olympic Stadium at an advanced
stage of construction in August 2010.

The Westfield Shopping Centre, Stratford, under construction in August 2010. When completed in 2011, developers claim that it will be one of the largest shopping malls in Europe.

A contrast in architectural styles: the brick-built 1960s flats in the foreground positioned in the shadow of a modern tower block, clad in glass and new building materials.

The rapidly changing scene across Stratford's Olympic Park as new buildings take shape to accommodate the world's leading athletes (August 2010).

Infrastructure changes below ground as new services are installed to support Stratford's growing number of buildings. In the foreground is a pipe-joining machine being prepared for operation.

The former West Ham Technical Institute, established in 1898, now part of the University of East London's Stratford Campus.

A choice of destinations within Stratford's Olympic Park.

The University of East London, Dockland Campus. Here students have the opportunity to study in modern surroundings at the Architecture and Visual Arts School; the Business School; the School of Computing, Information Technology and Engineering; and the School of Social Sciences, Media and Cultural Studies.

types of food available, our standard of medical care and the plethora of electronic communication both audible and visual. Just an upward glance will show Newham's rapidly changing skyline with the onward march of steel, glass, concrete and brick.

So let us maintain the continuity of our ancestors' endeavours that has brought us to this stage in our development. We must make sure we each hand over to the next generation something of quality, something sustainable that may become the catalyst for future regeneration within the Lea Valley, returning the region to its former place on the world innovation stage.

APPENDIX: PLAN UNVEILED BY BORIS JOHNSON FOR £30M SIEMENS PAVILION

In September 2010, just as I completed the last chapter in this book and was about to send the manuscript to my publisher, the Mayor of London, Boris Johnson, announced a revolutionary scheme to boost the economy of East London and create up to six thousand new jobs. As the scheme represents a perfect example of the "continuing progression" that I have been writing about it was impossible to forego the opportunity of recording the event, particularly as the company at the heart of the initiative was the technologically driven Siemens.

Artist's impression of the Siemens Pavilion.

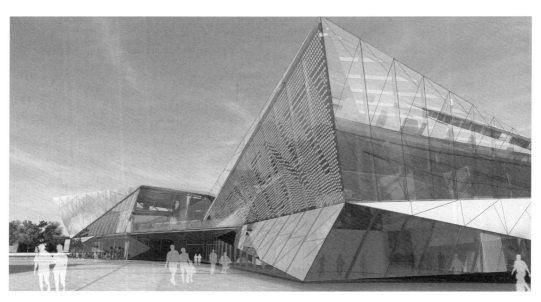

Artist's impression of the Siemens Pavilion at its site in Docklands.

Siemens plc, or Siemens Brothers & Company, was founded in 1858 by the German, William Siemens, who subsequently became a British citizen. In 1883 he was knighted by Queen Victoria for the service he rendered to "the cause of science". Now Siemens is a highly respected engineering company with factories and offices throughout the UK employing some 17,000 people.

The plan for London's East End is to create a 'Green Enterprise District' that will include the boroughs of Hackney, Tower Hamlets, Newham, Waltham Forest, Barking, Dagenham and Havering, designed to attract organisations that are involved in the low-carbon goods and services sectors. Also, it is planned to create an environment across the region that will encourage new businesses to start up in areas such as waste management, recycling, renewable energy, alternative fuels and building technologies. The focus of the initiative will be the £30m iconic Siemens Pavilion constructed as a sustainable building and located at the western end of the Royal Docks, close to London City Airport. Planned to open in early 2012, ahead of the London Olympics, the Pavilion will incorporate a 300-seat auditorium, an exhibition centre to showcase sustainable technologies, as well as a café and shop. Siemens are hoping that the Pavilion will attract around 100,000 visitors annually, made up of school groups and members of the public, and it is no secret that the company wishes to encourage young people to become immersed in the new sustainable technologies that will be crucial to the future survival of our planet.

Artist's impression of the Siemens Pavilion at night.

Artist's impression of the Siemens Pavilion with the O2 arena in the background.

SS Faraday, specifically designed to be the first ship in the world equipped to lay Siemens submarine cables.

Below left: Siemens Works at Woolwich, c.1915.

Below right: Cable coiling at Siemens Brothers, c.1920.

REFERENCES

From Monks to Modernity – Newham's Continuing Progression

Author unknown, *The Big Dig, Archaeology and the Jubilee Line Extension*, Museum of London Archaeology Service, London, 1998

Cox, Marjorie, Interview, June 2002

Evans, F.T., *Monastic Multinationals: the Cistercians and other Monks as Engineers*, Vol. 68, the Newcomen Society, 1996-7

Fry, Katharine (edited by G. Pagen), *History of the Parish of East & West Ham*, London, 1888

Morris, John (ed.), *Domesday Book, Essex*, Phillimore & Co., Chichester, 1983

Powell. W.R. (ed.), *The Victoria History of the County of Essex*, Vol. 6, Institute of Historical Research, University of London, 1973

Sainsbury, Frank, *West Ham 1886 - 1986*, Council of the London Borough of Newham, 1986

Sandon, Henry, *Flight & Barr Worcester Porcelain Company 1783-1840*, the Antique Collectors Club, 1978

Britain's First Commercial Porcelain Factory

Bernard, W., *The American Side, English Blue & White*, Faber & Faber, 1963

Powell, W.R. (ed.), *West Ham 1886-1986*, Council of the London Borough of Newham, 1986

Solon, M.L., *A Brief History of Old English Porcelain*, Bemrose & Sons Ltd., 1903

Tait, Hugh, *The Bow Factory under Alderman Arnold & Thomas Frye (1747-1759)*, a paper read at the Rembrandt Hotel (Mr And Mrs J.A. Wilby) on 8 February 1962

Walter Hancock

Author unknown, *The Telcon Story*, the Telegraph Construction & Maintenance Company Limited, 1950

Belmont James, J.L., *Centenary of Hancock's Steam Carriage, The India-Rubber Journal*, 30 May 1936

Hancock, Walter, *Narrative of Twelve Years' Experiments (1824 - 1836)*, John Weal, Architectural Library, London, 1838

Hancock, Walter C., 'Charles Hancock - Artist and Inventor', *Chemistry and Industry*, 30 September 1950

Lee, Sidney (ed.), *Dictionary of National Biography*, Smith Elder & Co., 1909

Lewis, Jim, *London's Lea Valley, Britain's Best Kept Secret*, Phillimore & Co. Ltd., 1999

Powell, W.R., *The Victoria History of the County of Essex*, Vol. 6, Oxford University Press, 1973

White, William, *Gazetteer and Directory of Essex*, Robert Leader, Sheffield, 1848

The Great Eastern Railway Works

Aldrich, Langley, *The Locomotives of the Great Eastern Railway – 1862-1962*, C. Langley Aldrich, Essex, 1969

Allen, Cecil, *The Great Eastern Railway*, Ian Allan, London, 1976

Author unknown, Memoranda connected with the Locomotive and Carriage Works at Stratford and the Wagon Works at Temple Mills, Great Eastern Railway, London, June 1921

Farmer, Jack, *The Great Eastern Railway as I Knew It*, J.R. Farmer, Theydon Bois, 1990

Gordon, W.J., *Our Home Railways – The Great Eastern Railway*, Vol. 1, Frederick Warne & Co., London, 1910

Hawkins, Chris and Reeve, George, *Great Eastern Railway, Part One – Stratford, Peterborough & Norwich Districts*, Wild Swan Publications Ltd., Oxford, 1986

Lewis, Jim, *Battleships, Buses and Bombers – a history of transport in the Lea Valley*, Libri Publishing Ltd., 2009

Pember, Geoffrey, *Great Eastern Railway 0-4-4 Tank Locomotives*, Great Eastern Railway Society, London, 1979

Sainsbury, Frank, *West Ham 1886-1986*, Council of the London Borough of Newham, London, 1986

The Thames Ironworks

Banbury, Philip, *Shipbuilders of the Thames and Medway*, David and Charles, Newton Abbot, 1971

Falconer, John, *What's Left of Brunel*, Dial House, Surrey, 1995

Lewis, Jim, *Battleships, Buses and Bombers – a history of transport in the Lea Valley*, Libri Publishing Ltd., 2009

Mackrow, G.C., 'Some Reminiscences of the Early Days of the Thames Iron Works and Shipbuilding Company', *Thames Iron Works Gazette*, Vol. 1, 1895

Mackrow, G.C., 'Some Reminiscences of the Early Days of the Thames Iron Works and Shipbuilding Company', *Thames Iron Works Gazette*, Vol. 2, 1896

Powell, W.R. (ed.), *West Ham 1886-1986*, Council of the London Borough of Newham, London, 1986

Sir Joseph Bazalgette

Bazalgette, Joseph William, 'On the Main Drainage of London and the Interception of the Sewage from the River Thames', *Minutes of Proceedings of the Institute of Civil Engineers*, 14 March 1865, Vol. 24 (1864-5)

Bazalgette, Joseph William, 'Address of Sir J.W. Bazalgette, President', *Minutes of Proceedings of the Institute of Civil Engineers*, 8 January 1844

Clayton, Antony, *Subterranean City Beneath the Streets of London*, Historical Publications, 2000

Lee, Sidney (ed.), *Dictionary of National Biography*, Joseph Vol. XXII, Smith Elder & Co., 1909

Lewis, Jim, *London's Lea Valley: Britain's Best Kept Secret*, Phillimore & Company Ltd., 1999

Lewis, Jim, *Water and Waste – four hundred years of health improvements in the Lea Valley*, Libri Publishing Ltd., 2009

The London Docks and George Parker Bidder

Author unknown, 'Memoirs of Deceased Members', *Minutes of Proceedings of the Institution of Civil Engineers*, Vol. 57, 1879

Bidder, George Parker, 'On Mental Calculation', *Minutes of Proceedings of the Institution of Civil Engineers*, 19 and 26 February 1856, Vol. 15, 1855–6

Powell, W.R. (ed.), *The Victoria History of the County of Essex*, Vol. 6, Institute of Historical Research, University of London, 1973

Sainsbury, Frank, *West Ham 1886-1986,* Council of the London Borough of Newham, 1986

Stephen, Leslie and Lee, Sidney (ed.), *Dictionary of National Biography*, Vol. II, Smith Elder & Co., 1908

Appendix: Plan unveiled by Boris Johnson for £30m Siemens Pavilion

Keogh, Anne, Head of External Relations Communications & Government Affairs, Siemens plc, conversation, 11 November 2010

Middlemis, Brian, *Siemens Brothers Engineering Society – Archive Collection*, Greenwich Industrial History Society Newsletter, Vol. 8, Issue 1, January 2005

Siemens press release, September 2010

The Siemens Engineering Society

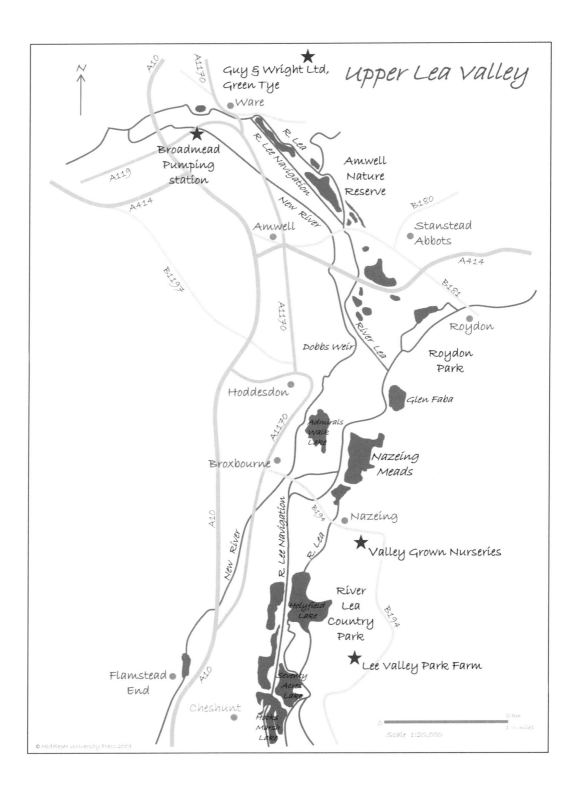

Upper Lea Valley

N

A10
A1170
★ Guy & Wright Ltd,
Green Tye
● Ware
★ Broadmead
Pumping
station
R. Lea
R. Lee Navigation
A119
New River
A414
B197
A1170
Amwell ●
Amwell
Nature
Reserve
B180
Stanstead
Abbots ●
A414
B181
River Lea
Dobbs Weir
Roydon ●
Roydon
Park
Hoddesdon ●
Glen Faba
A1170
Admirals
Walk
Lake
Nazeing
Meads
Broxbourne ●
B194
Nazeing ●
A10
New River
R. Lee Navigation
R. Lea
★ Valley Grown Nurseries
River
Lea
Country
Park
B194
Holyfield
Lake
★ Lee Valley Park Farm
Flamstead ●
End
A10
Seventy
Acres
Lake
Cheshunt ●
Hooks
Marsh
Lake

0   2 Km
                     1 ½ miles
Scale 1:20,000

© Middlesex University Press 2009

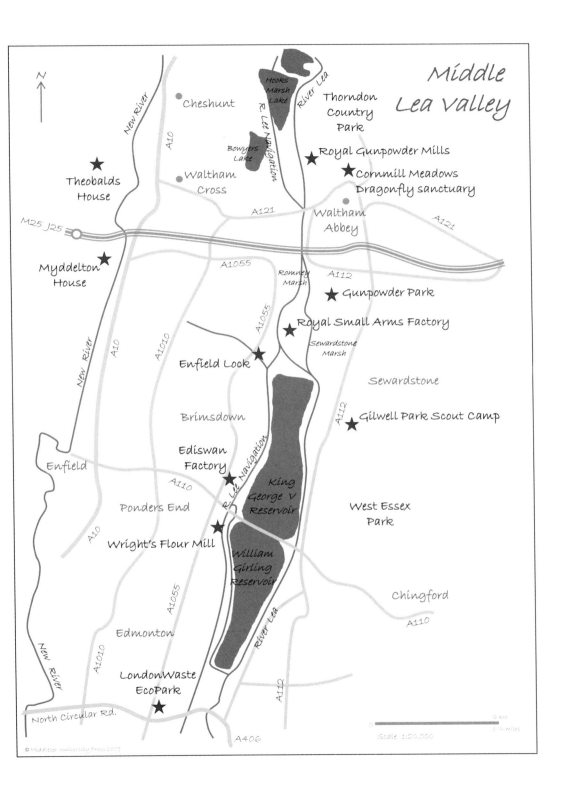

N

Middle
Lea Valley

New River

A10

Cheshunt

Theobalds
House

Waltham
Cross

R. Lee Navigation

Hooks
Marsh
Lake

River Lea

Thorndon
Country
Park

Bowyers
Lake

Royal Gunpowder Mills

Cornmill Meadows
Dragonfly sanctuary

M25 J25

A121

Waltham
Abbey

A121

Myddelton
House

A1055

Romney
Marsh

A112

Gunpowder Park

A10

A1010

New River

A1055

Royal Small Arms Factory

Enfield Lock

Sewardstone
Marsh

Sewardstone

Brimsdown

A112

Gilwell Park Scout Camp

Ediswan
Factory

Enfield

A110

Ponders End

Lee Navigation

Ri

King
George V
Reservoir

West Essex
Park

A10

Wright's Flour Mill

William
Girling
Reservoir

Chingford

A110

A1055

A1010

Edmonton

River Lea

A112

New River

LondonWaste
EcoPark

North Circular Rd.

© Middlesex University Press 2009

A406

Scale 1:20,000

2 km

1½ miles

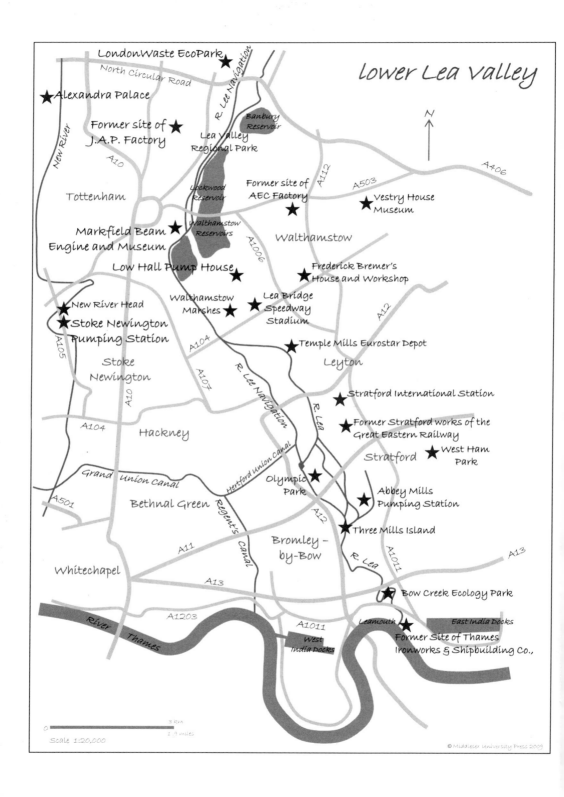